THE TIMES

times2 Crossword

Book 4

Compiled by John Grimshaw

This edition published 2010
First published in 2010 by Times Books as
The Times2 Crossword Book 14

HarperCollins*Publishers*
77–85 Fulham Palace Road
Hammersmith
London W6 8JB

www.collins.co.uk

© Times Newspapers Limited 2010

1

The Times is a registered trademark of
Times Newspapers Ltd

ISBN 978–0–00–788572–5
A catalogue record for this book is available from the
British Library

Layout by Susie Bell, www.f-12.co.uk

Printed and bound in Great Britain by
Clays Ltd, St Ives plc

Mixed Sources
Product group from well-managed
forests and other controlled sources
www.fsc.org Cert no. SW-COC-001806
© 1996 Forest Stewardship Council

FSC

FSC is a non-profit international organisation established to
promote the responsible management of the world's forests.
Products carrying the FSC label are independently certified
to assure consumers that they come from forests that are
managed to meet the social, economic and ecological needs
of present and future generations.

Find out more about HarperCollins and the environment at
www.harpercollins.co.uk/green

Introduction

This new collection of eighty *Times2* crosswords is selected from those published in *The Times* during 2005. With an average of about twenty-five per puzzle, that gives you close to two thousand clues to while away the hours. Precisely how many hours' time will depend on the individual solver, but the puzzles are not intended to try to catch you out with overly-obscure answers.

General knowledge is perhaps the aspect of the puzzle that generates the most correspondence from solvers. In the past year this even spilled over into the Feedback page of *The Times*, with opinions being given as to whether or not the word 'gamelan' was too obscure. As it had appeared in the puzzle, I must have felt it wasn't too difficult for an occasional appearance, but the person raising it clearly disagreed enough to write in. The exchange finished with one writer reporting that his teenage son was playing in a gamelan orchestra at school, and it wasn't a hard word at all, neatly exemplifying the range of familiarity I try to keep in mind when creating the puzzles.

As with the previous two volumes of puzzles, I have chosen the puzzles from among those designed with a bonus extra to be found in the completed grid. This puzzle feature is something that was started by the previous *Times2* Editor, Richard Browne, and I've continued it simply because it seems a fun thing to do. To give you an idea of the sort of thing I mean, after you've solved the first three puzzles you might like to look at the first letters in the across entries for Puzzle 1, find a hidden phrase in Puzzle 2 written around the grid in otherwise unchecked squares or think of a single word that can be linked to six of the entries in Puzzle 3. There's no compulsion to do this, of course, if what you want to do is simply to solve the puzzles.

In either case, I do very much hope you enjoy this latest volume.

John Grimshaw
Times2 Crossword Editor
May 2010

The Puzzles

ACROSS

1 Thigh bones (6)

5 St Columba's monastery (4)

9 Italian rice dish (7)

10 Story in instalments (6)

11 Puccini's Chinese opera (8)

12 Hark (6)

15 Indicate (6)

18 Buying out of one company by another (8)

20 Office worker (6)

22 Inspect thoroughly (7)

23 Enclosed part of building (4)

24 Shocked (6)

DOWN

2 Prolonged reprimand (*informal*) (6)

3 Not having used a razor (8)

4 Fully satisfied (5)

6 More than; finished (4)

7 Piece of music appropriate to the dawn (6)

8 Expensive (6)

13 Wheat pudding (8)

14 Long upholstered seat (6)

16 One who derives pleasure from spying on others (6)

17 Remove, erase (6)

19 Author of *Endymion* and *Ode to a Nightingale* (5)

21 Knowledge (*informal*) (4)

ACROSS

3 Set, become firmer (3)

8 Love affair (5)

9 Variant form of element (7)

10 Settle into warm position (7)

11 Wide tube-shaped pasta (5)

12 Unassuming; limited (6)

14 Highly-seasoned stew (6)

15 Silly person (*informal*) (6)

17 Extreme fear (6)

20 Beat; securing band (5)

21 Radioactive element (7)

24 Sudden increase (7)

25 Elevate (5)

26 Female sheep (3)

DOWN

1 Damages; planet (4)

2 Cheerful, light-hearted (6)

3 Spirits mixed with water (4)

4 Large ship (5)

5 Food warmer (8)

6 Investigate (2,4)

7 One going over to the opposition (8)

12 Curved upper surface of liquid in a tube (8)

13 Evasive like an eel (8)

16 Beat violently (6)

18 Dried grape (6)

19 Pulped vegetable or fruit (5)

22 4840 square yards (4)

23 Gentle, submissive (4)

ACROSS

1 Reduced to pulp (6)

4 Cooked in an oven (5)

8 Step (5)

9 Coffee whitener (7)

10 Zodiac sign (3)

11 Prefix meaning English (5)

12 Relating to numbers (7)

14 Grow more firm (6)

16 Road material (6)

20 Gracefully thin (7)

23 Hoarder of wealth (5)

24 Eisenhower's nickname (3)

25 Stealers (7)

26 Hanging rope (5)

27 Melodious; not bitter (5)

28 Outer garment (6)

DOWN

1 New England state (13)

2 Reel about; shock (7)

3 Fleshy appendage (3,4)

4 Freshwater fish (5)

5 Language of Cambodia (5)

6 DC in full (6,7)

7 Small cake (5)

13 Be incorrect (3)

15 River; academic (3)

17 Transcaucasian nation (7)

18 Was wrong about (item) (7)

19 Firm, dry, brittle (5)

21 Omit (syllable) (5)

22 Bed quilt (5)

3

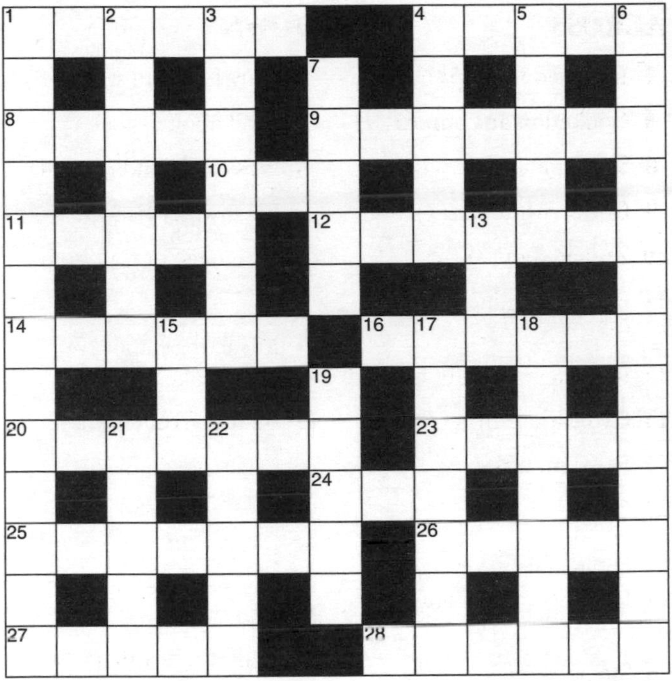

ACROSS

1 Evil sorcery (5,5)

9 Small flow (of liquid) (7)

10 Aboriginal native name for Ayers Rock (5)

11 Except that; single (4)

12 Caption at foot of foreign film (8)

14 Pungent bulb (6)

15 Light (a flame) (6)

18 TV set (*US informal*) (5,3)

20 Friend; chess move (4)

22 Indian city (5)

23 Vagrant; fishing boat (7)

24 Folded lower (10)

DOWN

2 Large area of water; pigment (4)

3 Bank order (6)

4 Large surplus stock (eg, of butter) (8)

5 Lean, haggard (5)

6 Controversial issue attracting public attention (5,7)

7 Resolute, determined (6-6)

8 Assassin (6)

13 Area of town or country (8)

16 Scarcity, lack (6)

17 Wallet (for papers) (6)

19 Relative by marriage (2-3)

21 Cycle (*informal*) (4)

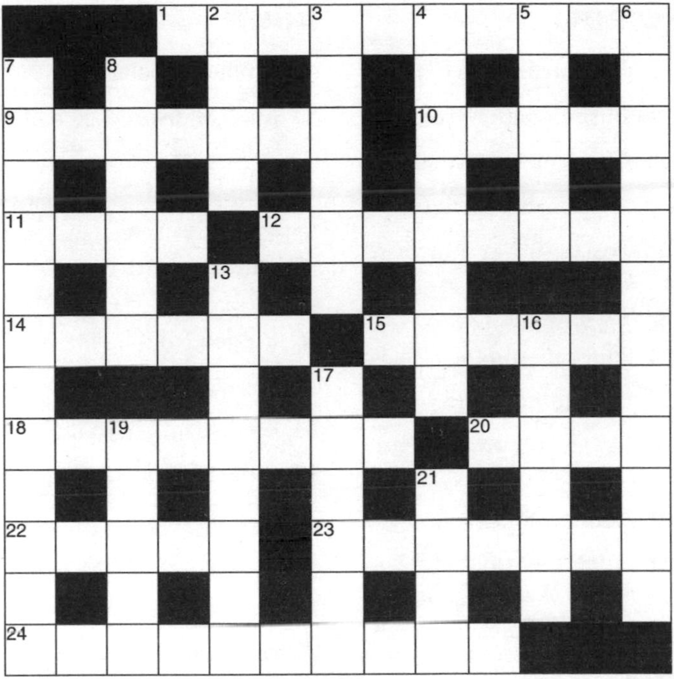
1
2
3
4
5
6
7
8
9
10
11
12
13
14
15
16
17
18
19
20
21
22
23
24

ACROSS

1 Digestive organ (7)

5 Basin; wooden ball (4)

8 Genuine; respectable (6)

9 Loud disturbance (6)

10 Post beside entrance (4,4)

12 State of mind (4)

13 Instrumental part not to be omitted (9)

17 Spanish-American farm labourer (4)

18 Fungus (8)

20 Rupert —, poet killed in World War I (6)

21 Nut (6)

23 Lump of earth (4)

24 US city and state (3,4)

DOWN

2 Edible flatfish (6)

3 Mass of disordered hair (3)

4 Approximately (*Latin*) (5)

5 One measures pressure (9)

6 Eg, gun (6)

7 Sweet; hypocrite (6)

11 English folk hero (5,4)

14 Clinging mollusc (6)

15 Fuel oil (6)

16 — Regis, West Sussex (6)

19 Climb; flake off (5)

22 Hawthorn blossom (3)

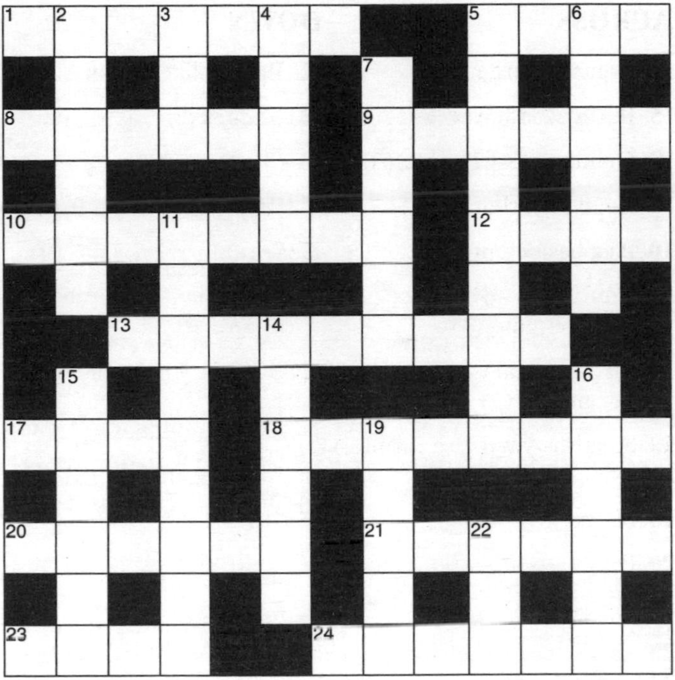
1
2
3
4
5
6
7
8
9
10
11
12
13
14
15
16
17
18
19
20
21
22
23
24

ACROSS

1 Commonplace (7)

5 Seize; start burning (5)

8 Horseman's weapon (5)

9 Reply (7)

10 Aggressive dog (3)

11 Courage in adversity (9)

12 Length of hose or pipe (6)

14 Six feet (in depth) (6)

17 Prevent (plan) from being fulfilled (9)

18 Tin (3)

19 In fact (whether by right or not) (2,5)

20 Last Greek letter (5)

21 Relating to countryside (5)

22 Shell used for decoration (7)

DOWN

1 Weasel-like mammal (7)

2 Keeper (5)

3 (They) exist (3)

4 Paralysing poison (6)

5 Severely reprimand (9)

6 More than is tolerable (3,4)

7 Boundary of bushes (5)

11 Excessively zealous (9)

13 One trying to deceive (7)

15 Written authority (7)

16 Antonio —, Italian sculptor (6)

17 Studio volume control (5)

18 Statement of belief (5)

20 Reproductive cells (3)

times2 Crossword **6**

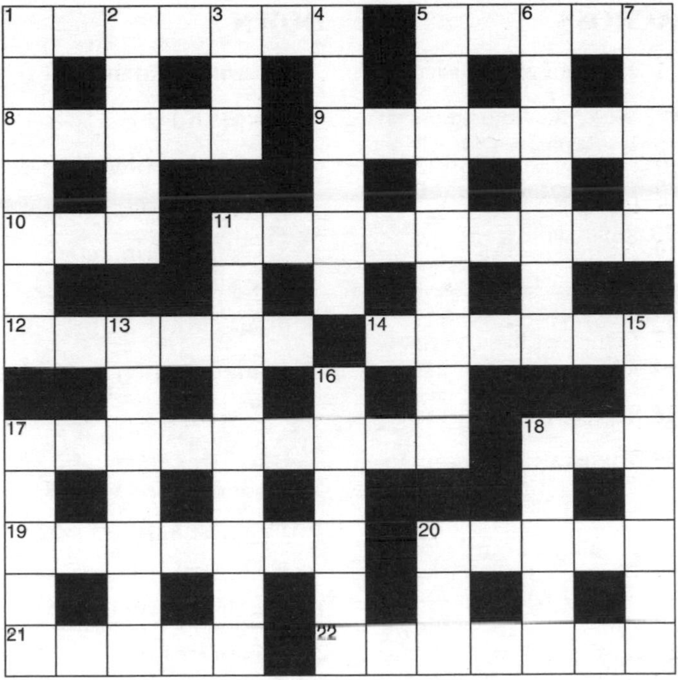

ACROSS

1 Jerome Kern musical (4,4)

5 Eve's partner (4)

9 Intoxicating liquid (7)

10 Small willow (5)

11 Baby carriage (4)

12 Chic (7)

14 Closest to the centre (6)

16 To rear (of a ship) (6)

19 Tumbler (7)

21 Large person (4)

24 Academy award (5)

25 — Rattigan, playwright (7)

26 Organs of sight (4)

27 Large sherry glass (8)

DOWN

1 Hit with the palm (4)

2 Take place (5)

3 West Indies island group (7)

4 Finally (2,4)

6 The killing of a god (7)

7 Trader (8)

8 Marine fish; rhymes with *fable* (4)

13 Apron (8)

15 God-inspired event (7)

17 Vigorous musical movement (7)

18 Lacking movement (6)

20 Skin of tree (4)

22 Vladimir Ilich Ulyanov (5)

23 Malt and hops drink (4)

times2 Crossword 7

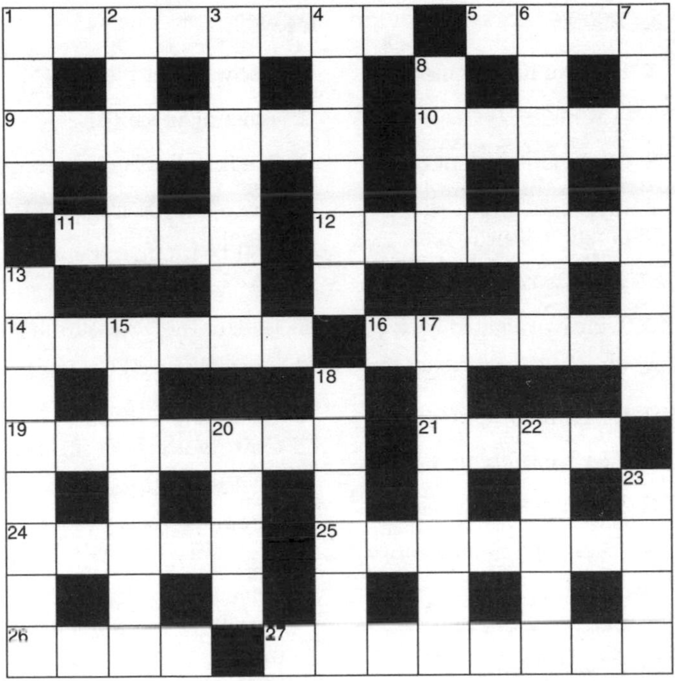

ACROSS

1 Piece of information (5)

7 A rebuke (7)

8 Ornamental plant (7)

9 Intellectual (*informal*) (7)

11 With two equal parts (6)

13 Security (against loss) (9)

15 With unbroken view (9)

19 Image recorder (6)

21 Like some cream (7)

23 Self-inflicted loss (3,4)

24 Lining up (awaiting turn) (7)

25 Undersides of feet (5)

DOWN

1 Michelangelo statue (5)

2 Twisting force (6)

3 Breakfast dish (6)

4 Steep hillside (*Scots*) (4)

5 Child with dead parents (6)

6 William —, 18th century English engraver (7)

10 Celtic language (6)

12 Cover with close-fitting surround (6)

14 Room for receiving guests in a monastery (7)

16 Have better weaponry than (another person) (6)

17 French film festival resort (6)

18 Spring back (in horror) (6)

20 Book of charts (5)

22 Venetian chief (4)

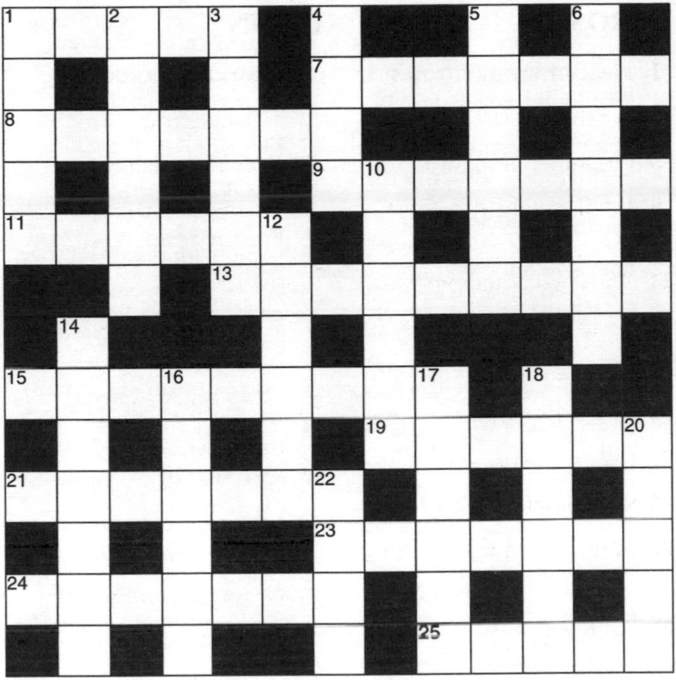

ACROSS

1 The throwing of a coin to decide outcome (4-2)

5 Person incorporating mechanical elements (6)

8 Very long period (4)

9 Rouse again (8)

10 M. C. —, Dutch graphic artist (6)

12 French military cap (4)

15 Crazy, mad (*informal*) (5,3,5)

16 Russian emperor (4)

17 Word aiding meditation (*Buddhism*) (6)

19 Lengthen (8)

21 Way of operation (4)

22 Dismiss (as faulty) (6)

23 Outlying city district (6)

DOWN

2 Protectors of footwear (9)

3 Mortal error (3)

4 Speak at length (8)

5 Punched paper; African nation (4)

6 Australian native bird (5,4)

7 Fish eggs; small deer (3)

11 Obstacle (9)

13 Mail service horseman (9)

14 Without joins (8)

18 Avoid food; rapid (4)

20 Untruth (3)

21 Disorderly crowd (3)

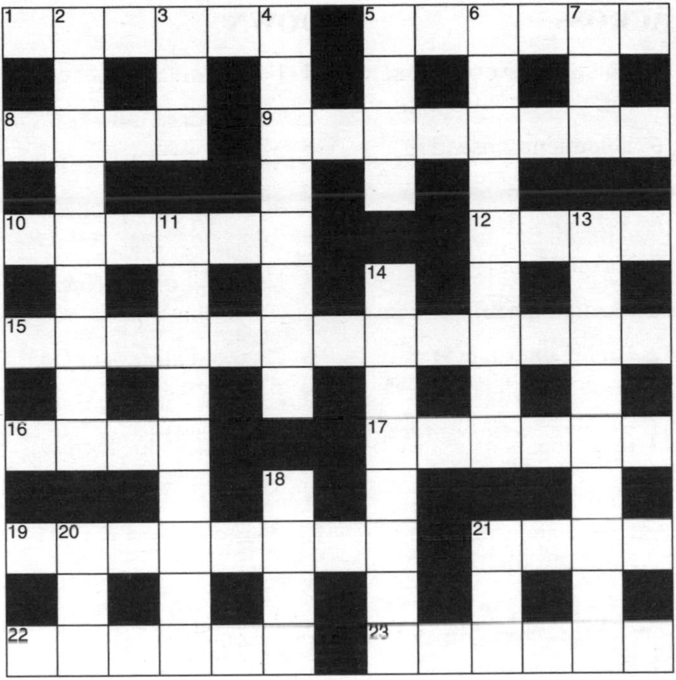

ACROSS

1 Make (problem) worse (9)

6 Solemn promise (3)

8 Highly repugnant (5)

9 Aircraft flap for slowing (7)

10 Acidic fruit (6)

12 Highly unusual (5)

13 Become visible (6)

14 Inflatable mattress (3,3)

17 Welsh dog breed (5)

19 Long-haired ruminant of Northern tundra (4,2)

21 Article used in part payment for another (5-2)

22 Winnie-the-Pooh author (5)

23 Water barrier (3)

24 Italian restaurant (9)

DOWN

1 Female relative (4)

2 Action done for show (7)

3 Some; whichever (3)

4 Solution (to a problem) (6)

5 Financial management (9)

6 Personal attendant (5)

7 Explosive missile part (7)

11 Not taking due care (9)

13 Aroused (7)

15 Young chicken (7)

16 Female name meaning lovable (6)

18 Kingdom (5)

20 Very large (*informal*) (4)

22 Encountered (3)

ACROSS

5 Charge with crime (6)

7 Country in Europe and Asia (6)

9 Difficult to move (8)

11 Attendant (4)

12 Cause to fall from horse (5)

13 Method, orderliness (6)

15 Lamentation (6)

17 Lazy person (5)

19 Long doleful cry (4)

20 Having the same opinion (8)

22 Inner part of nut (6)

23 Cause (someone) to suffer loss of dignity (6)

DOWN

1 State of central US (6)

2 Nought (4)

3 Small narrow opening (6)

4 Beat; raspberry stem (4)

6 Vegetable (11)

8 Highest mountain in England (*Lake District*) (7,4)

10 Indian cuisine cooked in two-handled dish (5)

14 Give out a bright light (5)

16 Closely; almost (6)

18 Administrator for monarch who is a minor (6)

19 (Price) increase; walk (4)

21 Offensively impolite (4)

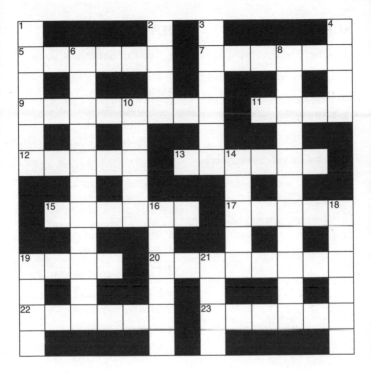

ACROSS

3 Wise, prudent (8)

7 Savoury party fare (6)

8 Persuade by coaxing (6)

9 Move busily (6)

10 Funny in a slightly peculiar way (*informal*) (6)

11 Notch (4)

13 Large African antelope (5)

15 US ten-cent coin (4)

17 Name shared by Monet, Debussy (6)

18 Powerful (6)

19 Reverend Awdry's Tank Engine (6)

20 Division of Yorkshire (6)

21 Lenience (8)

DOWN

1 Traditional Japanese drama (6)

2 Béla —, 19th-20th century Hungarian composer (6)

3 West African republic (7)

4 Broke; drunk (*informal*) (7)

5 Green vegetable (8)

6 All people (8)

11 Addictive drug (8)

12 Deeply unconscious (8)

13 Final stage of play (*chess, bridge*) (7)

14 Children's room (7)

15 Ridicule (6)

16 Tomorrow (*Spanish*) (6)

ACROSS

1 Eastern European 24 *ac* (5)

4 Mexican 24 *ac* (7)

8 One buying and selling (9)

9 Unwell (3)

10 — Armstrong, first man to set foot on the Moon (4)

11 American 24 *ac* (8)

13 Shelter for aircraft (6)

14 Mental image (of future) (6)

17 Indian fare akin to 24 *ac* (8)

19 Visible mark of healing (4)

22 Medic (*informal*) (3)

23 Walking leisurely (9)

24 Shrove Tuesday fare (7)

25 Thin 24 *ac* (5)

DOWN

1 Relay race stick (5)

2 Native of Turin (7)

3 Individual article (4)

4 Fall headlong (6)

5 Brief summary (8)

6 Part of psyche (5)

7 Waterproofed cloth (7)

12 Southeast Asian country (8)

13 Stimulated, excited (*informal*) (5,2)

15 Slope (7)

16 Rude, vulgar (6)

18 Nut (5)

20 Unprincipled man (5)

21 Allied group of countries or political parties (4)

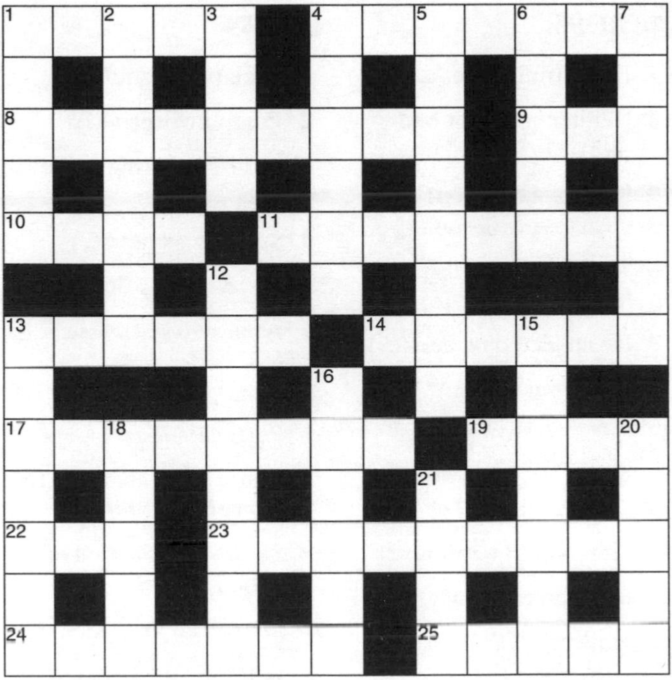
1
2
3
4
5
6
7
8
9
10
11
12
13
14
15
16
17
18
19
20
21
22
23
24
25

ACROSS

1 Hold firmly together (6)
4 Neither good nor bad (2-2)
7 Lady — Hamilton, mistress of Nelson (4)
8 Thomas —, English furniture-maker (8)
9 It's collected by bees (6)
10 Contribution (5)
11 Cease to have physical presence (13)
14 One less than 19 *ac* (5)
15 London rail terminus (6)
17 Beat (an adversary) (8)
18 French for north (4)
19 One more than 14 *ac* (4)
20 Have ambition (to achieve something) (6)

DOWN

1 Take part (in race) (7)
2 Pumping organ (5)
3 Act of restoring to life (12)
4 Surgeon's blade (7)
5 Uncivil; brief film (5)
6 Ability to settle issues (12)
12 Southern region of Portugal (7)
13 Cause great suffering to (someone); whip (7)
14 Short stanza at end of ballade (5)
16 Mount where Moses received Commandments (5)

ACROSS

1 Very hot green chilli (8)

6 In favour of (3)

8 Noël Coward play (6,6)

9 Grasped, carried (4)

10 Painted rear stage cloth (8)

12 Assault; pester (6)

14 Vegetable gourd (6)

16 Approximately 2.205 lb (8)

18 Hope earnestly (for particular outcome) (4)

20 Arrangement between vendor and supplier (4,2,6)

22 Beer (3)

23 Injured by many blows (8)

DOWN

2 Leisurely walk (5)

3 She helped Theseus against the Minotaur (7)

4 One showing items in gallery display (9)

5 Operations (*informal*) (3)

6 Worked steadily at (a trade) (5)

7 Venezuelan river (7)

11 Soft French cheese (9)

13 Japanese island captured by US in June 1945 (7)

15 Intense joy (7)

17 Very overweight (5)

19 — *Get Your Gun*, musical (5)

21 *Ay, there's the —* (*Hamlet*) (3)

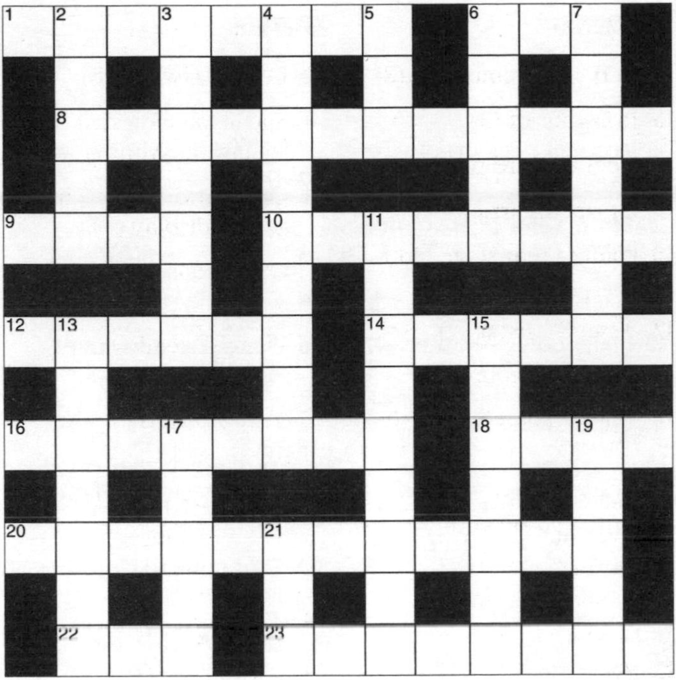

ACROSS

1 (Of blow) bouncing off (8)

5 Ancient neck ornament (4)

8 Hard water pipe coating (3)

9 Back of neck (4)

10 Height of excellence (4)

12 Visitor reporting point (9,4)

13 — Wharf; — yellow (6)

14 Pressurise (someone to do something) (*informal*) (4,2)

17 Eating bugs (13)

20 Was aware of (4)

21 Prong (4)

22 In the manner of (*French*) (1,2)

23 Usual standard (4)

24 Making metallic ring (8)

DOWN

1 Attack (someone); decide on (an option) (2,3)

2 Eg, someone from Zaire (7)

3 Secret plan (10)

4 Serviette (6)

6 At the right moment (2,3)

7 Airport register point (5-2)

11 Second wife of Henry VIII (4,6)

13 Bird; coward (*informal*) (7)

15 Modern Hitlerite (3-4)

16 Relating to son or daughter (6)

18 Contemptuous gesture (5)

19 Informal language (5)

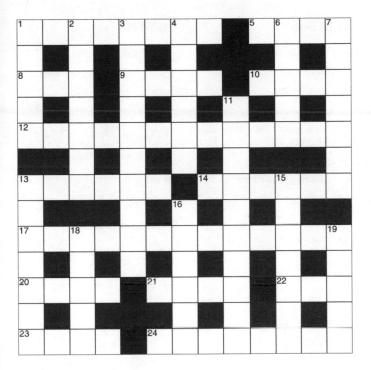

ACROSS

1 Move, stir (5)

4 Religious day (7)

8 Brushed dirt collector (7)

9 Die in water (5)

10 Bravery (12)

12 — *and Cleopatra* (*Shakespeare*) (6)

13 (Of land) waterlogged (6)

16 Familiar with many cultures (12)

18 Nuclear weapon (1-4)

20 Supporters' group (3,4)

22 Cheese (7)

23 Fast (5)

DOWN

1 Of poor quality (3)

2 Downward slope (7)

3 International language (9)

4 Tanning lounger (6)

5 Bottom of river (3)

6 Stopped sleeping (5)

7 Plant; truthfulness (7)

11 Writing materials seller (9)

12 Old-fashioned (7)

14 Traffic jam (*informal*) (5-2)

15 Player on links (6)

17 Reserve; shop (5)

19 Offer (at auction) (3)

21 Unopened flower (3)

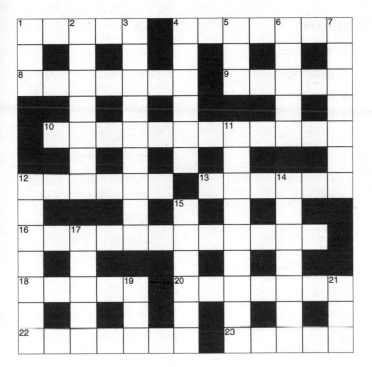

ACROSS

1 Young men (6)

5 Meeting list (6)

8 (Ancient Greek) portico (4)

9 Buried waste material (8)

10 Innards of fowl (7)

11 Relating to city or town (5)

13 Driving licence penalty (11)

16 Beaver-like animal (5)

18 *Bad money drives out good* is his law (7)

21 Jester in *The Tempest* (8)

22 Take off (a hat) (4)

23 Promotional notice (6)

24 Eagerly, enthusiastically (6)

DOWN

2 Exterior (7)

3 Beaten path; be in losing position (5)

4 Single (8)

5 Relative (4)

6 Compel compliance with (law) (7)

7 Wing shape; Greek D (5)

12 Annual publication (8)

14 Mozart's librettist for *Don Giovanni*; *O pedant* (*anagram*) (2,5)

15 Inclined to cry (7)

17 Like a rowing boat (5)

19 Walk furtively (5)

20 Cause pain to (4)

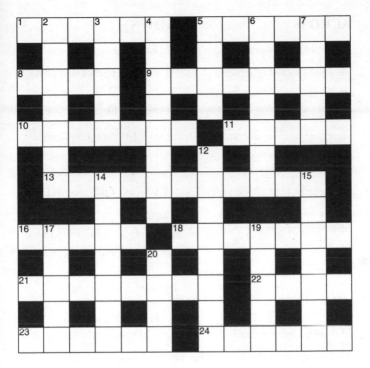

ACROSS

1 Tease; silly person (4)

4 In direction of breeze (8)

8 Critic (8)

9 Academic robe (4)

10 Sir Thomas —, 16th century English poet and diplomat (5)

11 Insect killer (3,4)

13 Divergence from course (6)

15 Sister's son (6)

18 Strong laminated board (7)

20 Least well (5)

23 Language element (4)

24 Of any kind (8)

25 Late winter flower (8)

26 Aslant; bias (4)

DOWN

2 Thin, puny (*informal*) (5)

3 Swindler; tornado (*US*) (7)

4 First light (4)

5 (Of birds) singing softly (8)

6 Worker's earnings (5)

7 Former London prison (7)

10 Existed in the past (3)

12 Armed sailing ships (3-2-3)

14 Native of southern Belgium or northern France region (7)

16 Bravery in battle (7)

17 Saturated (3)

19 One who has lost husband (5)

21 European; vegetable (5)

22 Stinging insect (4)

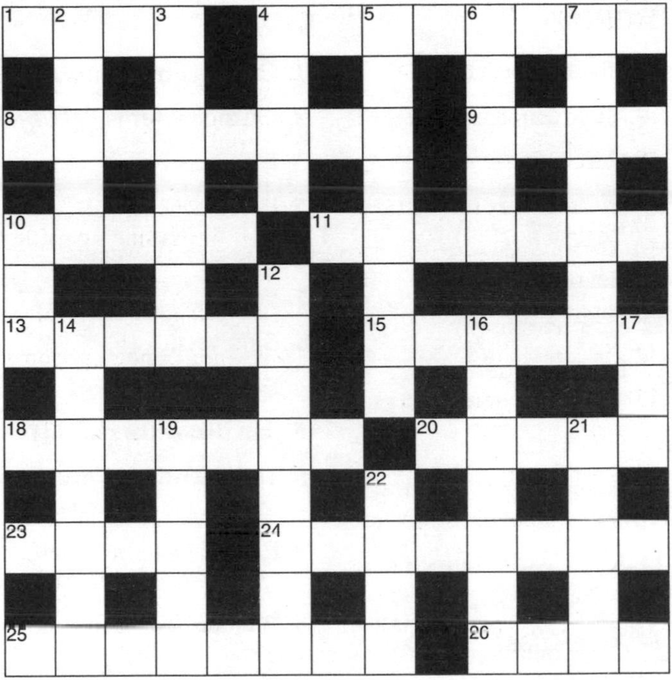
1
2
3
4
5
6
7
8
9
10
11
12
13
14
15
16
17
18
19
20
21
22
23
24
25
26

ACROSS

1 Divide in two (6)

4 Move fast; missile (4)

9 Cut (meat) (5)

10 Andrew —, 17th century English poet (7)

11 Hair cleanser (7)

12 Slow learner (5)

13 Possible ordering (of a number of items) (11)

17 Piles (5)

19 Major Isle of Wight town (7)

22 At the earliest time (7)

23 Cat (*informal*) (5)

24 Carry out (command) (4)

25 1/1000 kg (*French*) (6)

DOWN

1 Opposes; males (5)

2 Outside layer (7)

3 Inexpensive (5)

5 Pure; hygienic (5)

6 (Of sound) sweet (6)

7 Persistent, pressing (11)

8 Believe; tick (6)

14 Edible mollusc (6)

15 American marsupial (7)

16 Treatment using massage or exercise (*informal*) (6)

18 Exclusively; by oneself (5)

20 Windscreen cleaner (5)

21 Aromatic herb (5)

ACROSS

6 Traditional English song (12)

7 Sentimental film (*informal*) (6)

8 Entangle (6)

9 — O'Brien, Irish novelist (4)

10 Height (above ground) (8)

12 Without rest (8)

16 Unclothed (4)

18 Make pot of tea (4,2)

20 Invented; untrue (4-2)

21 Camera fitment (for remote operation) (5,7)

DOWN

1 Memento (8)

2 Intestines (*Greek*); *neater* (*anagram*) (6)

3 Most advanced in age; *led set* (*anagram*) (6)

4 Give the impression of being (4)

5 Became vaguely aware of (something) (6)

6 Selfish desire (5)

11 Unable to perceive musical pitch accurately (4-4)

13 Radio waves receiver (6)

14 Die (6)

15 Figure of speech, eg, as cool as a cucumber (6)

17 Two (at cards) (5)

19 In good health (4)

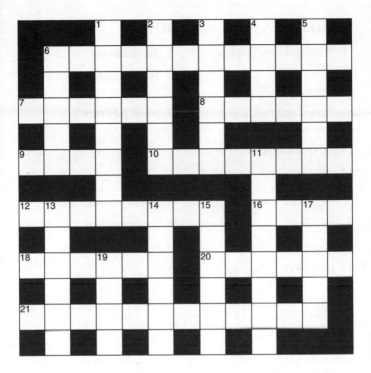

ACROSS

1 Balloon (for drinking) (6,5)

8 Paris river (5)

9 Period of broadcast transmission (7)

10 Jump (with rope) (4)

11 Classical name for Switzerland (8)

13 Capital of Saudi Arabia (6)

14 Suave, refined (6)

17 Destined for bad luck (3-5)

19 Public bathing beach (4)

22 Porridge ingredient (7)

23 Category (of things) (5)

24 Far from moderate state (11)

DOWN

1 Foundation (5)

2 Ability to move quickly (7)

3 Squirrel's nest (4)

4 Using toothed wheels (6)

5 Ant-eating mammal (8)

6 Long-legged wader (5)

7 Public discussion (6)

12 Adjoining (8)

13 Horned mammals (6)

15 Having life (7)

16 — Howard, British actor (*Gone with the Wind*) (6)

18 Potato pancakes (in Jewish cookery) (5)

20 Fertile desert spot (5)

21 Dart-playing line (4)

ACROSS

3 Botanic gardens site (3)

8 Boadicea's tribe (5)

9 Of the distant past (7)

10 Without purpose (7)

11 Remove fastenings (5)

12 (Of words) become fully understood (4,2)

14 Male or female germ cell (6)

15 An uncommon thing (6)

17 — Puddleduck (*Beatrix Potter*) (6)

20 Make basketwork (5)

21 Survive beyond (another) (7)

24 Cause to operate (7)

25 Swiss mathematician (5)

26 Rowing blade (3)

DOWN

1 Peruvian capital (4)

2 Toady (3,3)

3 Toy; bird of prey (4)

4 Narrow part of body (5)

5 Correct in all details (8)

6 Water boiler (6)

7 And so on (2,6)

12 Proposition to be argued over (5,3)

13 As good as done (2,3,3)

16 Bridge in Venice (6)

18 Hanging ice (6)

19 Juliet's lover (5)

22 Level (in hierarchy) (4)

23 Book of the Old Testament (4)

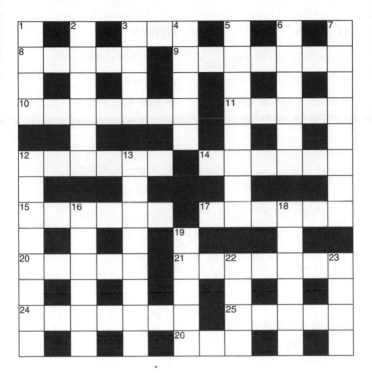

ACROSS

1 Bad-tempered (6)

4 Kremlin location (6)

8 Encourage development of (a child) (7)

10 Nervous excitement; high temperature (5)

11 Muslim ruler (4)

12 Brief evocative description (8)

14 Prepared state (9)

18 Cairo native (8)

20 Cloak; promontory (4)

22 Synthetic fabric (5)

23 Zero degrees latitude (7)

24 Container for brewing up in quantity (3,3)

25 Farm implement; school (6)

DOWN

1 £10 note (*informal*) (6)

2 Small dog (7)

3 Pull with effort (4)

5 Law breaker (8)

6 Cat; musky perfume (5)

7 Prison guard (6)

9 Completely remove (9)

13 Eg, clip, catch (8)

15 Break suddenly (7)

16 Substance to curdle milk (6)

17 Sketch again (6)

19 Churchill, Roosevelt and Stalin met here in 1945 (5)

21 Deep brass instrument (4)

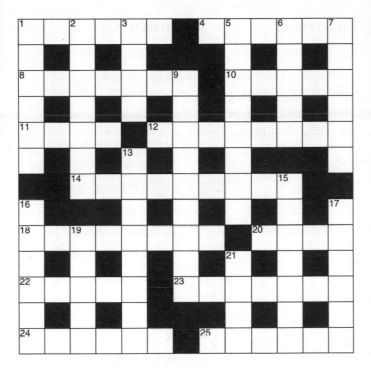

ACROSS

7 Move stealthily (as tiger) (5)

8 Shoer of horses (7)

9 Competitive way of life (3,4)

10 Cock fattened for eating (5)

11 Kiln (4)

12 One honoured for outstanding achievement (8)

15 Supersonic airliner (8)

16 Pacific republic (4)

19 (Of requirement) not fulfilled (5)

21 Frightened (7)

22 Publicly ridicule (7)

23 Immature insect form (5)

DOWN

1 Wine city in Portugal (6)

2 Black line on London underground map (8)

3 Sir Edward —, English composer (5)

4 Delicate ornamental stonework (7)

5 Small strand (4)

6 Citrus fruit (6)

8 Informal, relaxed (4-3-4)

13 Scots ski resort (8)

14 Mail receptacle (7)

15 Small groups (of trees) (6)

17 Delhi native (6)

18 Underground chamber (5)

20 West African country (4)

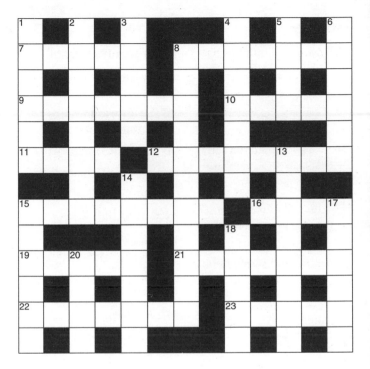

ACROSS

7 Row of stables (4)

8 Homeric hero (8)

9 Soonest (8)

10 Swedish pop group (4)

11 Small in width (6)

13 Celestial object emitting great energy (6)

15 Elevation (6)

17 Rowing boat race; 8 8 (6)

19 The same (as that just mentioned) (*Latin*) (4)

21 Light (a fire) again (8)

23 Flower container (4,4)

24 Appearance, manner (4)

DOWN

1 Eastern US state (8)

2 Inn attendant (*historical*) (6)

3 Solitary; sounds like *advance* (4)

4 Fascinating quality (8)

5 Spain for Spaniards (6)

6 Without sensation (4)

12 1815 battle (8)

14 *The Netherlands* — are islands in the Caribbean (8)

16 Cocktail; borer (6)

18 Organism's complete genetic material (6)

20 Pairs (4)

22 Potter's oven (4)

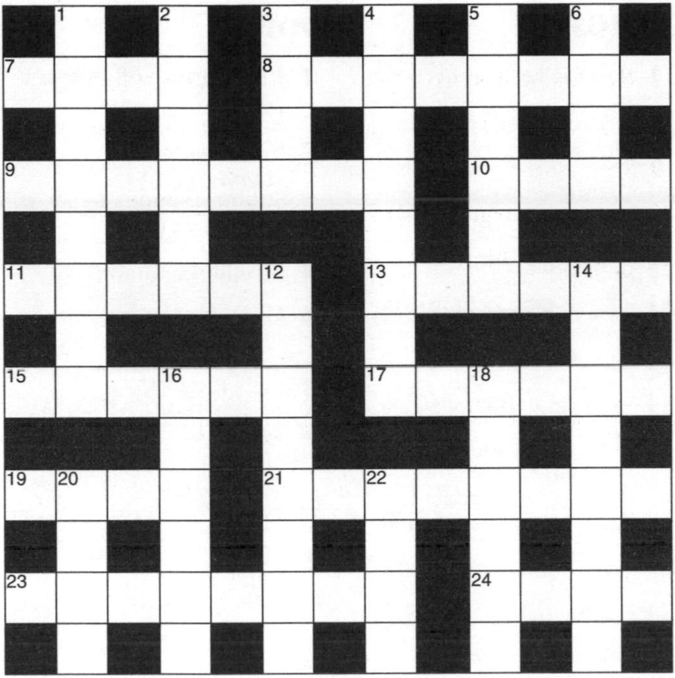
1
2
3
4
5
6
7
8
9
10
11
12
13
14
15
16
17
18
19
20
21
22
23
24

ACROSS

1 Site for vertical take-off (8)

5 Not genuine (4)

9 Walled-court ball game (7)

10 Over (5)

11 Taxi passenger; food (4)

12 Et cetera (3,2,2)

14 — Day; — bunny (6)

16 Deal with; name (*informal*) (6)

19 Illegal game hunter (7)

21 Long-eared animal (4)

24 Indian dish (5)

25 Take for granted (7)

26 Tough (4)

27 Within the body (8)

DOWN

1 Large group of animals (4)

2 — *di Lammermoor* (*Donizetti*) (5)

3 Go before (7)

4 Mischievous child (6)

6 Human-seeming robot (7)

7 Put at risk (8)

8 Source of river; leader (4)

13 Send off; kill (8)

15 One shirking work (7)

17 Sportsman (7)

18 Arrive for casual visit (4,2)

20 Restore to health (4)

22 City of Normandy (5)

23 Actually existing (4)

ACROSS

7 Muse of history (4)

8 Dismiss as foolish (4-4)

9 Eugene —, US playwright (*The Iceman Cometh*) (6)

10 Mother of Sir Galahad (6)

11 Two-masted ship (4)

12 Showing appreciation (8)

15 Carefully looked after (4-4)

17 (Military) assistant (4)

18 Edible marine fish; *sea pad* (*anagram*) (6)

21 (Of baby) not delivered (6)

22 Roman philosopher (*Consolation of Philosophy*) (8)

23 David Copperfield's 'child-wife' (4)

DOWN

1 Medieval Scandinavian (3,5)

2 Pugilism (6)

3 Final part of book (8)

4 Debauchee (4)

5 Drug (6)

6 Midday (4)

13 Selfless helper of others (8)

14 Low type of throw (8)

16 Shed built against wall (4-2)

17 Measure of reflectiveness; *doable* (*anagram*) (6)

19 One looking down on others (4)

20 Mine access passage (4)

ACROSS

1 Early form of paper (7)

5 Elephant monarch of children's literature (5)

8 Language of southern India (5)

9 Of the same kind (7)

10 Island state of Australia (8)

11 — Laurel, comedian (4)

13 Four-sided figure (13)

16 Miner's lamp inventor (4)

17 Relating to drama; actor (8)

20 Victorian street light (3,4)

21 Polite address to woman (5)

22 Smart, fashionable (*informal*) (5)

23 Song-like (7)

DOWN

1 Car race service break (3,4)

2 American wild cats (5)

3 Trustworthy (8)

4 Vatican site of frescoes by Michelangelo (7,6)

5 Explosive device (4)

6 Strengthen; pillow (7)

7 Show (eg, film) again (5)

12 Fine spider's silk (8)

14 Go back to (place) (7)

15 Of a smallest amount (7)

16 Begin eating heartily (3,2)

18 Group of languages including Sanskrit (5)

19 New-born child (4)

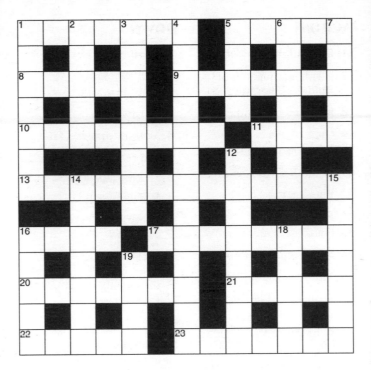

ACROSS

1 Placc to stay on holiday (8)

5 Manufacture (4)

8 Matched (8)

9 Each of two (alternatives) (4)

11 Recorded film (5)

12 Plunder, rob (7)

13 Reddish-brown; apple (6)

15 Solicitor, barrister (6)

18 Moved (position) (7)

19 Samuel —, 17th century diarist (5)

21 Finishes (4)

22 Make free (8)

23 Encounter (4)

24 Car safety strap (4,4)

DOWN

1 Meat axe (7)

2 Hillock (5)

3 Outline representation (10)

4 With it (*informal*) (6)

6 Expression of regret (7)

7 — Merman, US musical comedy star (5)

10 Steep slope at edge of plateau (10)

14 Fraudulent scheme (7)

16 Deep admiration (7)

17 Guidance (6)

18 Water vapour (5)

20 Tranquillity (5)

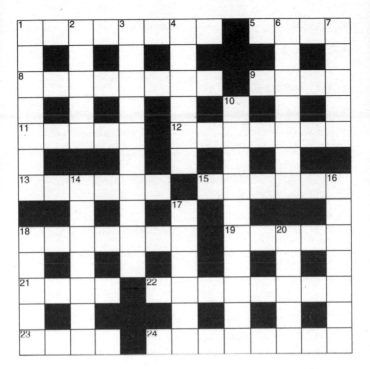

ACROSS

1 Dorset peninsula with limestone quarries (8)

5 City; tub (4)

8 Hanging seat; jazz style (5)

9 Scots dress item (7)

11 Unit of work (3)

12 Oil (a mechanism) (9)

13 Precious metal (6)

15 Alive; income (6)

18 Dramatised TV programme based on real events (9)

19 Star (3)

20 (Of law) legally binding (2,5)

21 Impertinence (*informal*) (5)

22 Pavement edging (4)

23 (Of corn) not reaped (8)

DOWN

1 Have (7)

2 Regretting (5)

3 Money which must be accepted as payment (5,6)

4 1645 Royalist defeat (6)

6 Small aircraft for hire (3,4)

7 Door pivot (5)

10 Innate tendency to evil (8,3)

14 Satan (7)

16 Medicinal tonic root (7)

17 Mourn; express regret (6)

18 Eg, beer (5)

19 Riyadh native (5)

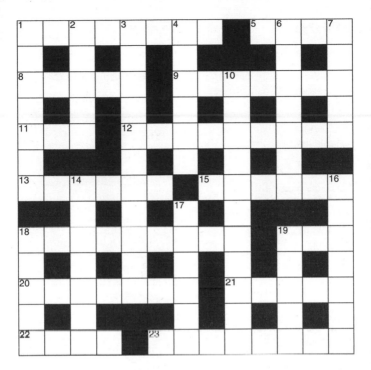

ACROSS

1 Popular piscine pet (8)

5 River forming part of German-Polish border (4)

9 Conduct causing non-physical suffering (6,7)

10 Port of Yemen (4)

11 Salad vegetable (7)

13 In official records (2,4)

15 Stefan —, tennis player (6)

18 Make less heavy (7)

20 Word indicating action (4)

23 Remover of hardness (eg, from mains supply) (5,8)

24 Impudent, cheeky (4)

25 Drama written for TV (8)

DOWN

1 Jewels (4)

2 (Of paper) ruled (5)

3 Face-cloth (7)

4 Feed (baby) from breast (6)

6 Rid of lice (7)

7 English physicist; *hairy leg (anagram)* (8)

8 Musical piece for two (4)

12 Subsequent addition (6-2)

14 Military aircraft (7)

16 Fan (7)

17 Repeat performance (6)

19 School year division (4)

21 Of the kidneys (5)

22 (Of weather) cloudy (4)

ACROSS

2 (Of accent) precisely enunciated (3,5)

6 Again reverberate (2-4)

8 Ship; container (6)

9 Releasing (7)

10 Torquato —, 16th century Italian poet (5)

12 Slides in music between two notes (10)

16 Former nickname of Edinburgh, 'old smoky' (4,6)

18 Errol —, swashbuckling film actor (5)

20 Lumpy (7)

21 Train; group of fish (6)

22 Formal address (6)

23 Supermarket carts (8)

DOWN

1 With a cheerful manner (7)

2 English county (8)

3 *In the* — (*Elvis Presley*) (6)

4 Fools; quadrupeds (5)

5 Large public room (6)

7 Eg, bishop, knight (8)

11 Bring together (8)

13 Gloom (8)

14 Mound (7)

15 Amount by which something is out of line (6)

17 Not fashionable (*informal*) (6)

19 Rude or brutish person (5)

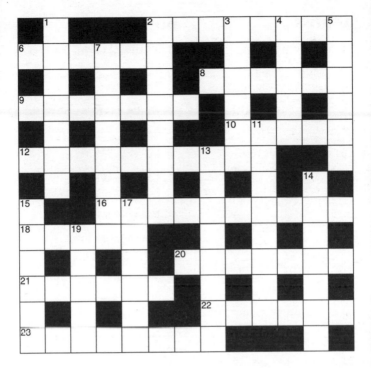

ACROSS

1 Vatican head (4)

3 Cistern valve (8)

9 Carroll's heroine (5)

10 (As gem) many-sided (7)

11 Moving vehicles (7)

12 Christmas (4)

14 Cook (egg) in water below boiling point (6)

16 Personal history (6)

18 — Morecambe, comic (4)

19 Obsessive enthusiast (7)

22 Wide area (7)

23 Raccoon-like animal of Central and South America (5)

24 Spread throughout (8)

25 Flood embankment (4)

DOWN

1 Doctor's business (8)

2 Formal and correct (4,3,6)

4 Make a difference to (6)

5 Permit; freedom (7)

6 Far from it (2,3,8)

7 Captain William —, Scottish pirate (4)

8 Meat; complaint (4)

13 Be engaged in (profession) (8)

15 Authorise (something) (7)

17 Bring about (6)

20 Narrow connecting part (4)

21 (Of sound) low in pitch (4)

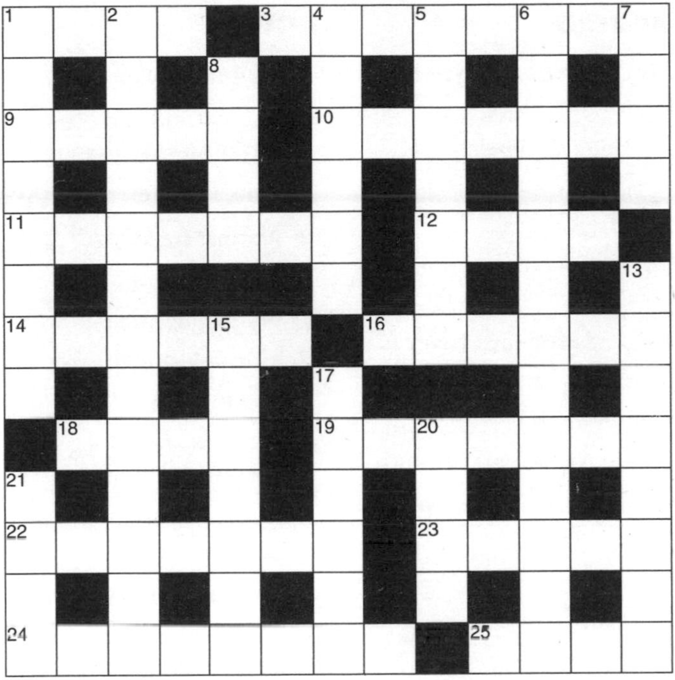
1
2
3
4
5
6
7
8
9
10
11
12
13
14
15
16
17
18
19
20
21
22
23
24
25

ACROSS

1 One overstating danger (8)

5 Reduce to pulp (4)

9 Complete; unabridged (5)

10 Affirm faith in (religion) (7)

11 One providing cover (7)

12 Repair clumsily (*informal*) (5)

13 Conversation (9)

18 Pacific island group (5)

20 Valve operator in internal-combustion engine (7)

22 Sign, omen (7)

23 Pasta sauce variety (5)

24 Regard, consider (4)

25 Human-made article (8)

DOWN

1 Egyptian jackal-headed god (6)

2 Charged with offence (7)

3 Travel by car; engine (5)

4 Powerful calculator (13)

6 Make corrections to (eg, document) (5)

7 Move quickly (6)

8 Thief (6)

14 Male organ of flower (6)

15 Large landmass combining two continents (7)

16 Lacking common sense (6)

17 Clever, skilful (6)

19 Sensation transmitter (5)

21 Franz von —, Austrian light opera composer (5)

ACROSS

1 (Of lines) moving apart (9)

6 Alphabet (3)

8 Evergreen conifer (7)

9 Indicate by suggestion (5)

10 Challenge (of courage) (4)

11 Ornamental chain (8)

13 Deviation from tempo (*music*); *or tuba* (*anagram*) (6)

14 Prelude to Bless you! (6)

17 Barking and —, London borough (8)

18 *Miss — Regrets* (*song*) (4)

20 Plants (of a region) (5)

21 Make, manufacture (7)

22 Name for Pluto or hell (3)

23 Departure from accepted standards (9)

DOWN

1 One interpreting cipher (7)

2 Bristly wild plant (6,7)

3 Tall water-loving grass (4)

4 Happened afterwards (6)

5 Cogitating (8)

6 Closest star to the Sun (5,8)

7 Glasgow's river (5)

12 Flag; norm (8)

15 Oriental (7)

16 Anatoly —, former Russian chess champion (6)

17 Region of southwest Wales (5)

19 Long seat (4)

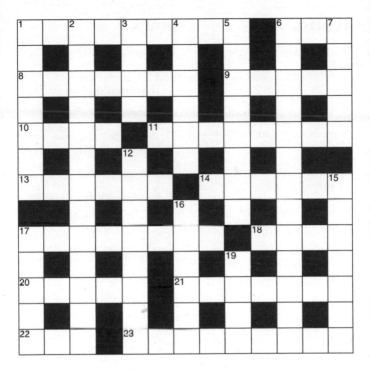

ACROSS

1 Cows and oxen (6)

7 Concurred (6)

8 Notable (8)

10 Escape after crime (7)

11 Relating to stars (7)

12 Tall conifer (5)

14 Solemnly promise (5)

15 *Uncle* — (*Le Fanu*); — *Marner* (*Eliot*) (5)

19 Breed of African hunting dog that rarely barks (7)

20 Fortress (7)

22 Hover in the air (8)

23 Napoleon died on St. — (6)

24 Feel; name (*informal*) (6)

DOWN

1 Furrow, wrinkle (6)

2 Of the highest importance (3-5)

3 Unfortunate (8)

4 As are drakes, bulls etc (4)

5 Mysterious (6)

6 State of western US (6)

9 Pleasant, pleasing (9)

12 *Troilus and* — (*Shakespeare*) (8)

13 Toper, sot, lush (8)

16 In the same source (*Latin*) (6)

17 Bright-flowered shrub (6)

18 Ancient rowed warship (6)

21 Style, enthusiasm (4)

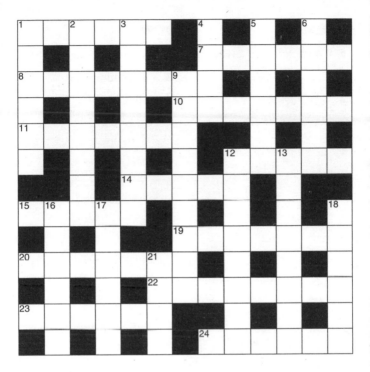

ACROSS

1 *What's New, —? (Woody Allen film)* (8)

5 Play music in street (4)

7 Venus before sunrise (7,4)

8 Short golf shot (4)

9 Intensely cold; beer (6)

10 Envelop (6)

13 Tub; tax (3)

14 British soldier recruited overseas (6)

17 Horse-drawn vehicle (6)

18 Rapid (4)

19 Limiting condition (11)

20 Scots valley (4)

21 Wife to Orpheus (8)

DOWN

1 Boxer's training item (8)

2 Retail outlet (4)

3 College of arts (13)

4 Test of verbal dexterity (6-7)

5 Confer (an honour) (6)

6 Ancient Greek city known for warlike spirit (6)

7 Male form of address (6)

11 Type of sleeve (6)

12 Hole (in tyre) (8)

15 Ill (6)

16 Long loose tunic (6)

18 Sustenance (4)

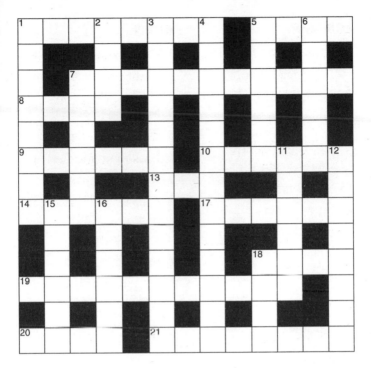

ACROSS

1 Particular emphasis (6)

4 Flying mammals (4)

8 Outer garment (8)

9 Stereo (2-2)

11 Compete (3)

12 Consequently (9)

13 Slim, supple (6)

15 Eg, mouse or squirrel (6)

18 Indecisive chess ending (9)

19 Secret agent (3)

20 Dark (4)

21 Humorist (8)

22 Looked at closely (4)

23 Resolve (dispute) (6)

DOWN

1 Slippery substance (5)

2 Baron von —, German World War I air ace (10)

3 Mounted (a play) (6)

5 Of tissue storing fat (7)

6 Backbone (5)

7 Nonsense (6)

10 Final revealing moment (10)

14 Shine brightly (7)

16 Annoying; sampling (6)

17 US gangster (*St Valentine's Day massacre*) (6)

18 Wading bird (5)

19 Show amusement or pleasure (5)

ACROSS

1 Meeting (needs, etc) (10)

7 Terrible tsar (4)

8 In one dimension; *I learn* (*anagram*) (6)

9 Sudden attack (of illness) (7)

10 Twining invasive plant (8)

11 Diving waterbird (5)

13 With plume on helmet (7)

14 Excellent (*informal*) (5)

17 Computer programmes (8)

18 Dirty; ritually impure (7)

19 Untamed horse (*US*) (6)

20 Male admirer; dandy (4)

21 Disorder, instability (10)

DOWN

1 Austrian city with annual music festival (8)

2 — Fork aids a musician (6)

3 Reliable, hard-working (8)

4 Implant (5)

5 Part of bird's stomach (7)

6 Capital of Croatia (6)

9 Studio recording period (7)

11 Pertaining to meaningful movements (8)

12 Letter cover (8)

13 Cry (4,3); summons to emergency repair visit (4-3)

15 Shoot; messenger (6)

16 Heavy gun (6)

17 One putting money by (5)

ACROSS

1 Fruit tree (6)

4 Unwanted plant (4)

7 Capital of Latvia (4)

8 (Of child) being taken on by foster parents (8)

9 Frank; undeviating (6)

10 Weighty (5)

11 One may be thus in love (4,4,5)

14 Ray (of light); access to mine (5)

15 Encourage, stir up (6)

17 Common hooting bird (5,3)

18 Filth (4)

19 German form like Mr. (4)

20 Like a rough cloth (6)

DOWN

1 Cooking style characteristic of a place (7)

2 Make ecstatically happy (5)

3 Act of restoration to functioning state (12)

4 Light bulb power rating (7)

5 Diplomatic messenger (5)

6 Relations gained by marriage (7-2-3)

12 Crockery drying rack (7)

13 Form of church service (7)

14 Thin; elegantly simple (5)

16 Try to get (something) without paying (5)

ACROSS

1 Effect of calming drug (8)

6 Ability to recognise and appreciate sounds (3)

8 State of being linked (12)

9 Actually existing (4)

10 Making changes (8)

12 Committed to memory (6)

14 Material used to block up hole (6)

16 Camping cooking pot (8)

18 Deep chasm (4)

20 Victoria's consort (6,6)

22 Cow's call (3)

23 Rearing ponds for, eg, salmon (4,4)

DOWN

2 Master of ceremonies (*mainly US*) (5)

3 Ring-shaped (7)

4 Firm, not springy (9)

5 Word of negation (3)

6 Young eel (5)

7 Pertaining to light-sensitive part of eye (7)

11 Three-sided figures (9)

13 Concise witty saying (7)

15 Greenery worn by Adam or Eve (3,4)

17 Slowly (*music*) (5)

19 Afterwards (5)

21 Small supernatural being (3)

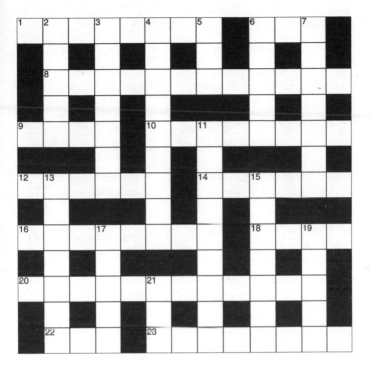

ACROSS

1 Society for singing part songs (4,4)

7 One relaxing (6)

8 Hole for, eg, shoe lace (6)

9 Turns in a wide circle (6)

10 Wallet for paper money (8)

12 Put up (7)

13 Group ethnically different from those around it (7)

16 Share in an undertaking (8)

17 (Of liquid) boil (6)

18 Insect (6)

20 Speak (poem) aloud (6)

21 (Of dog) fetch shot game (8)

DOWN

1 Expression of mild surprise (*mainly US*) (3)

2 What stops farm animals straying (8,5)

3 Persuade by force (6)

4 Beer maker (6)

5 Open-air drama (6,7)

6 Head of a republic (9)

10 Required (9)

11 Number of Wonders of the World (5)

14 One watching TV (6)

15 Body entering earth's atmosphere (6)

19 River flowing from Exmoor to Exmouth via Exeter (3)

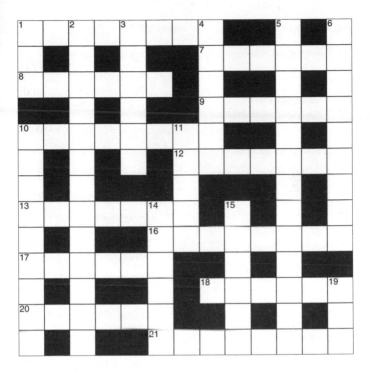

ACROSS

1 Long cloud of smoke (5)

4 Pickling condiment (7)

8 Afghanistan rulers 1995–2001; *lean bat* (*anagram*) (7)

9 (Pasta) cereal (5)

10 Alexander —, Russian novelist (*The Gulag Archipelago*) (12)

12 In good taste (6)

13 Peril with Charybdis (6)

16 Specifically (2,10)

18 Large cat (5)

20 Hindmost part (4,3)

22 New Zealand South Island port (7)

23 Apparition (5)

DOWN

1 Favourite (3)

2 Let free (7)

3 One misappropriating money (9)

4 Thin covering (of wood) (6)

5 At present (3)

6 Estimate, conjecture (5)

7 Round domed building (7)

11 Containing (9)

12 Very virtuous (7)

14 South American plains cowboy (7)

15 Young cat (6)

17 Heathen (5)

19 Unit of radiation (3)

21 Small spot (3)

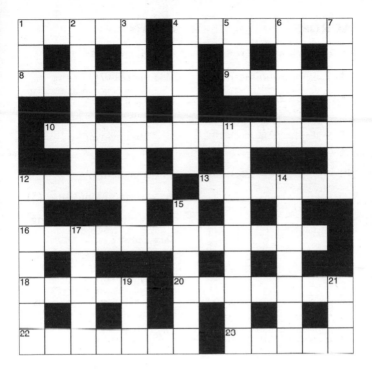

ACROSS

1 Relating to citizens (5)

7 Side view (of face) (7)

8 Mediterranean coastal region (7)

9 System of connections (7)

10 Unacceptable (*informal*) (3,2)

11 Reluctantly sanction (7)

13 Unit of quilt insulation (3)

15 Involuntary contraction (3)

17 Phoenician love goddess (7)

19 Fail (an exam candidate) (5)

21 Rearrangement of letters (7)

23 Items from distant lands (7)

24 Uncertain, puzzled (2,1,4)

25 Inuit canoe (5)

DOWN

1 Small crown (7)

2 — *Regina* was sung at Queen's coronation; long live (*Latin*) (5)

3 Sharply outlined (5-3)

4 Gospel writer (4)

5 Mosque tower (7)

6 Steady; flat; floor (5)

7 Eg, repaper, Hannah (11)

12 Accept too many reservations (for flight) (8)

14 Arthurian knight (7)

16 Place to leave vehicles (3,4)

18 Polite address to woman (5)

20 — cake; — godmother (5)

22 Top of car or house (4)

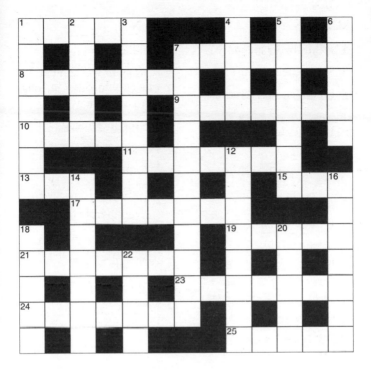

ACROSS

1 Utilisation (10)

7 Strangely (5)

8 Open meshed fabric (7)

10 Tiny — (*Dickens: A Christmas Carol*) (3)

11 Unending (9)

13 Showy flower (6)

14 Arm band (6)

17 Ordinal number (9)

19 Time-travelling Doctor (3)

20 Note near piano centre (6,1)

22 Sharp point on, eg, rose (5)

23 Driving (something) forward (10)

DOWN

1 (Of disease) regularly found in population (7)

2 One studying the nature of matter (9)

3 Room for business (6)

4 Mistress (*abbreviation*) (3)

5 Japanese trained assassin (5)

6 Examination of dead body (4-6)

9 Apposite (2,3,5)

12 Stringy pasta (9)

15 Make a mistake (2,5)

16 Writing instrument (6)

18 Duck with soft down (5)

21 Edge of mouth (3)

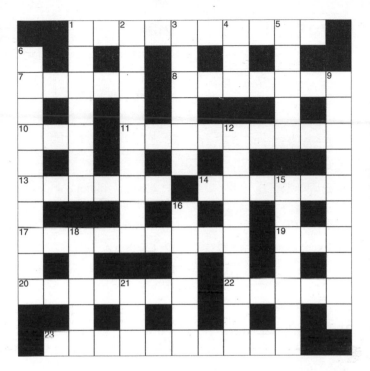

ACROSS

1 *In summertime on   /*
The bells they sound so
clear (*A. E. Housman*)
(6)

5 Shrill insect (6)

8 Repulsive to the eye (4)

9 Bird cages (8)

10 Frolicking (7)

11 Cleanse by running
water (5)

13 Exchanging places (11)

16 Formed (pot) on wheel
(5)

18 Exceptional (7)

21 Uniquely associated
(3-2-3)

22 Chimney vent (4)

23 Agreeably; respectably
(6)

24 Measure up for mapping
(6)

DOWN

2 Barbed fastener; *grab lot*
(*anagram*) (7)

3 Cease talking (3,2)

4 Proximity (8)

5 Wound length (of rope)
(4)

6 Arcangelo —, 17th-18th
century Italian composer,
violinist (7)

7 Squirrels' nests (5)

12 Earl's wife (8)

14 Inspiring reverential fear
(7)

15 Small compact particle
(7)

17 Capital of Vietnam (5)

19 Up to this point (2,3)

20 Dedicated to God (4)

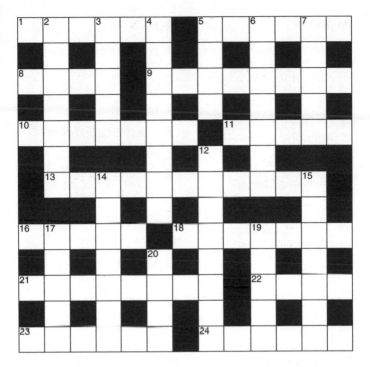

ACROSS

1 The — swine rushed into the sea (*Bible*) (8)

7 Cow's stomach as food (5)

8 Wars of the Roses house (9)

9 Negative answer (3)

10 Brief rush of wind (4)

11 Asserted openly (6)

13 In a haphazard manner (6)

14 Bully; Trojan warrior (6)

17 — Holst, English composer (6)

18 Was indebted (4)

20 Pub counter (3)

22 Try hard (to achieve) (9)

23 Soft lustre (5)

24 Setting of Psalm 51 (8)

DOWN

1 Soviet labour camp (5)

2 Line of rulers (7)

3 (Horse) of mixed colour (4)

4 Local inhabitant (6)

5 Evil demon (5)

6 Time around December 31 (3,4)

7 Fishing boat (7)

12 Make damp (7)

13 Flying station (7)

15 Cable used after breakdowns (3,4)

16 Indian political dynasty (6)

17 Welcome (someone) (5)

19 Song of lament for dead (5)

21 Female horse (4)

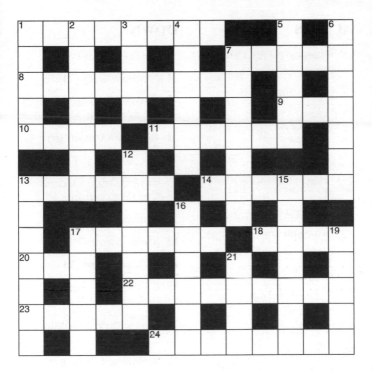

ACROSS

1 University area (6)

5 Part of bridge; 9 inches (4)

8 Wizard's rod (4)

9 Colourant (8)

10 Of sombre character (8)

11 Fragrant bulbous plant (4)

12 Whence Shakespeare's two gentlemen (6)

14 Small gadget (6)

16 Excessive supply (4)

18 Garden pest (8)

20 Floor covering (8)

21 Change form or state (4)

22 Tool; sounds like *sums* (4)

23 Forest keeper (6)

DOWN

2 Usually (2,1,4)

3 Military chaplain (5)

4 Common songbird of reed beds (5,7)

5 Resolved (an argument) (7)

6 Very bad (5)

7 Common bunting (12)

13 Consequence (7)

15 Make bigger (7)

17 Scottish owner of large estate (5)

19 — Costner, US actor (*Dances with Wolves*) (5)

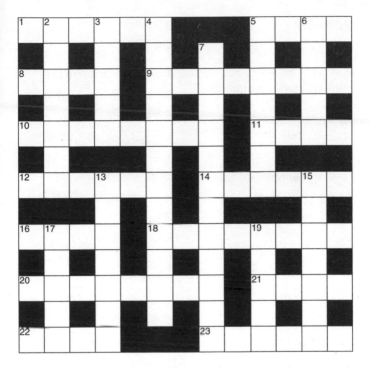

ACROSS

1 Victimise (someone) (4,2)

4 Importance; heaviness (6)

9 High area of level land (7)

10 Nation; I (*radio communications*) (5)

11 Turning machine (5)

13 Table support (7)

14 Coating in kettle (3)

15 Unit of heat (5)

16 It's mined for minerals (3)

17 Unvarying (7)

19 Top of ridge (5)

21 Temporary stop (5)

22 Violent person (7)

24 Detective (6)

25 Wanting food (6)

DOWN

1 Schoolchild (5)

2 Talk informally (7)

3 Bravo! (*Spanish*) (3)

5 Of skin's outer layer (9)

6 *Waiting for —* (*Beckett*) (5)

7 Acrobat's swing (7)

8 In addition; besides (11)

12 Outgoing person (9)

14 Social blunder (4,3)

16 Beginning; available job (7)

18 Accustom (someone) to something unpleasant (5)

20 Aromatic wild plant (5)

23 Influenza (3)

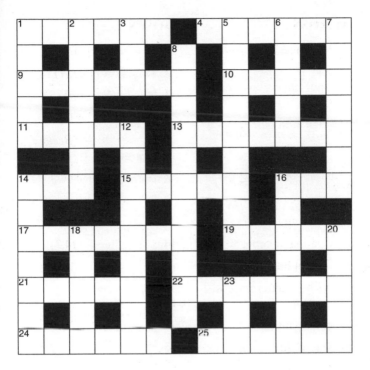

ACROSS

1 Senior churchman (10)

7 One providing food (7)

8 Section of waste pipe (1-4)

10 North Kent seaside resort (7)

11 Showing gross lack of sensitivity (5)

12 Not one person (6)

15 Course of meal (6)

17 Marie —, French physicist (5)

18 Athlete who jumps while running (7)

21 Telling falsehoods (5)

22 Monarch's use of the first person plural (5,2)

23 Variety of white wine (10)

DOWN

1 Daisy-like plant (5)

2 Magna — (*Runnymede, 1215*) (5)

3 Keg (6)

4 Very small quantity (7)

5 Outdoor (4-3)

6 Promoting unity between churches (10)

9 Cause (someone) to lose confidence (10)

13 Polish by rubbing (7)

14 Boat scooping up mud (7)

16 Town of northern Scotland (6)

19 Cellulose fabric (5)

20 Sweet; money (*informal*) (5)

ACROSS

1 Woven container (6)

4 Arrow projection (4)

9 Showery month (5)

10 Instructive comparison between two things (7)

11 A letter (7)

12 Odds offering equal chance of win or lose (5)

13 Recompense for loss (11)

17 Flat dish (5)

19 Noble, lofty (7)

22 Swiss cheese (7)

23 Tropical fruit (5)

24 Large jug (4)

25 Express agreement (6)

DOWN

1 William —, English poet, artist and visionary (5)

2 Continue to exist (7)

3 Red Sea resort (5)

5 House, home (5)

6 Youthful (6)

7 Round brackets (11)

8 Father or mother (6)

14 Academic dissertations (6)

15 Strong indignation (7)

16 Culmination, climax (6)

18 Critical; shrewd (5)

20 Pheasant; butterfly; 100-eyed monster (5)

21 Handed out (cards) (5)

ACROSS

1 Sir Ernest —, Irish-born Antarctic explorer (10)

8 (Of wit) sharp, critical (7)

9 Puccini's Roman heroine (5)

10 Nautical hailing call (4)

11 Organisation's influence in the community (8)

13 Ralph — Emerson, US poet and philosopher (5)

14 Ring-shaped reef (5)

16 Variant form (of gene) (8)

17 Fertile soil (4)

20 (Greek) market place (5)

21 Activated by wind (7)

22 One giving to a cause (10)

DOWN

1 Polynesian island group (5)

2 A danger to breathers (3,9)

3 Zen riddle (4)

4 Etch (3,3)

5 Sudden occurrence (of war, disease, etc) (8)

6 Entertainer getting free from constraints (12)

7 Andy —, 20th century US artist (6)

12 Varsity Putney to Mortlake contest (4,4)

13 Burrowing marsupial (6)

15 Give (transplant organ) (6)

18 Large country house (5)

19 Deep unconsciousness (4)

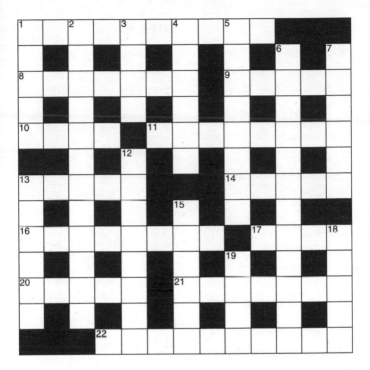

ACROSS

1 For example (4,2)

4 Brake or clutch perhaps (5)

8 SI unit of capacitance (5)

9 Train stop (7)

10 Region of south Germany (7)

11 Unit of memory size (4)

12 6th note of major scale (3)

14 13th-14th century Italian poet (5)

15 Valuable thing (5)

18 Catch (thief) (*informal*) (3)

20 Sliding window frame (4)

22 Old Testament Hebrew patriarch (7)

24 Utter repeatedly (7)

25 He was killed in his bath (5)

26 (Bird of prey's) claw (5)

27 Black eye (*informal*) (6)

DOWN

1 Convertible furniture (4,3)

2 Group crossing a desert (7)

3 Hans Christian — (8)

4 Loud ringing of bells (4)

5 Made from milk (5)

6 Sudden fencing thrust (5)

7 Habitual (5)

13 Clear the throat noisily (8)

16 Of an African desert (7)

17 Enticer (7)

19 Bread maker (5)

20 Overflowed (5)

21 Illegally take (5)

23 Farm building (4)

ACROSS

1 What's shared by close companions (11)

8 Deduce (from evidence) (5)

9 Less uneven; soft-soap (7)

10 Bound volume (4)

11 Stinging arachnid (8)

13 Predatory arachnid (6)

14 Mischievous child (6)

17 Commercial activity (8)

19 Stiff paper; comb (4)

22 Haifa native (7)

23 Portion; coin; item (5)

24 Fiercely-contested fight (6,5)

DOWN

1 Rise (in value, status) (5)

2 Sicilian criminals (7)

3 Delicate; casual (4)

4 Erase (from surface) (6)

5 Clearance below ceiling (8)

6 Bacteriologist giving name to culturing dish (5)

7 Strong spirit (6)

12 Change (something) so much as to appear new (8)

13 Yield; present (a proposal) (6)

15 Dishonest behaviour (7)

16 Eddying (6)

18 Clean; low vegetation (5)

20 Live (in a place) (5)

21 Incentive; branch line (4)

ACROSS

3 Sound of involuntary diaphragm contraction (3)

8 Record of events (5)

9 Fruit (7)

10 Severe; lacking comforts (7)

11 Trap (5)

12 Church district (6)

14 Purpose (6)

15 Pay back (money) (6)

17 Wildly excited state (6)

20 Chimney; pile (5)

21 US folk dance gathering (7)

24 Discharged (7)

25 Trojan war beauty (5)

26 Self-esteem (3)

DOWN

1 Notion (4)

2 Roman emperor's title (6)

3 Extravagant promotion (4)

4 One attending invalid (5)

5 Eg, Dr Crippen (8)

6 Deceptive appearance (6)

7 In unassuming manner (8)

12 Died (8)

13 Ancient Indo-European language (8)

16 (Of drink) iced, chilled (6)

18 Pasta strip (6)

19 Scold, rebuke (5)

22 Reverberate (4)

23 Not any (4)

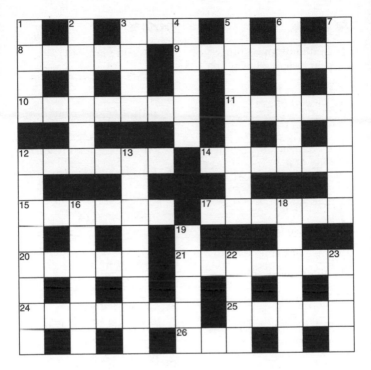

ACROSS

1 Clothes manufacturer (10)

9 Blood disorder (7)

10 Marie —, 19th-20th century English music-hall entertainer (5)

11 One of the Great Lakes (4)

12 Chicago's state (8)

14 Unearth (3,3)

15 More intimate (6)

18 Rather too liberal (8)

20 Slovenly person (*informal*) (4)

22 Relating to ends of the earth (5)

23 Material for making airtight or watertight (7)

24 (Of spectacles) giving idealised view (4-6)

DOWN

2 Slope; swindle (4)

3 Paper fastener (6)

4 Herman —, *Moby Dick* author (8)

5 Former Japanese capital (5)

6 Allocate differently (12)

7 Secret listener (12)

8 Identifying (6)

13 Scarper! (3,3,2)

16 Muslim sovereign (6)

17 Trafalgar victor (6)

19 — Island, former reception point for US immigrants (5)

21 Twelve bottles of wine (4)

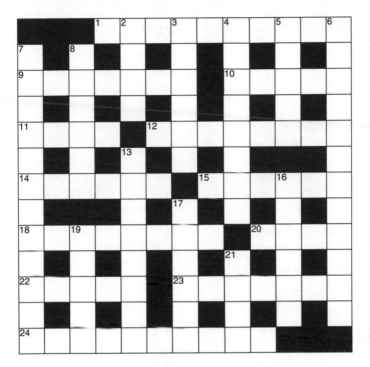

ACROSS

7 Give up (territory) (4)

8 Nereid (3,5)

9 Outlook putting the mind of man in central place (8)

10 American wild cat (4)

11 Drilling platform (3,3)

13 Buster —, US film comedian (6)

15 Over-fastidious person (6)

17 Chafed (6)

19 The Emerald — (*Ireland*) (4)

21 One disliking the new (8)

23 Put forward (as candidate for election) (8)

24 Calf flesh (4)

DOWN

1 Hampshire stately home (8)

2 Make good (6)

3 Fungal spore sacs; *I sac* (*anagram*) (4)

4 Forceful punch (*informal*) (8)

5 Short-sightedness (6)

6 Unwanted e-mail (4)

12 Good afternoon in German (5,3)

14 Overpower, overwhelm (8)

16 Spanish peninsula (6)

18 Act in a particular way (6)

20 Wintry weather (4)

22 Available for business; exposed (4)

ACROSS

1 Johann — , The Waltz King (or his father) (7)

5 Consecrate (5)

8 High male or low female voices (5)

9 Coin's head side (7)

10 Sheepdog breed (6,6)

12 Show connection between (things) (6)

14 Female name (6)

17 Irish bestower of persuasive speech (7,5)

21 Small particle (7)

22 Glowing piece of coal (5)

23 Short poem (5)

24 Strong stream (7)

DOWN

1 Sword sheath (8)

2 It lifts helicopter (5)

3 Not cleaned (7)

4 Decisively put an end to (6)

5 Sloped edge (5)

6 Item of jewellery (7)

7 Toboggan (*mainly US*) (4)

11 Confidentially (2,6)

13 Soothing song (7)

15 One rubbing and kneading painful muscles (7)

16 Imperfection (6)

18 Employ again (5)

19 Card game (5)

20 — Stravinsky, composer (4)

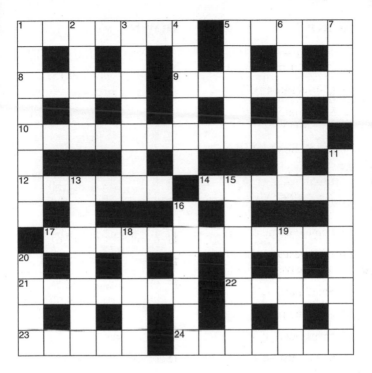

ACROSS

1 Discourse (6)

5 Openly resists (6)

8 Tree; waste away (4)

9 Lacking bravery (8)

10 Large property (6)

12 Atlantic alliance (*abbreviation*) (4)

15 US term for avocado (9,4)

16 Narrow channel (*Scots*); rhymes with *dossier* (4)

17 Painful big toe swelling (6)

19 Rapidly increase (8)

21 Not speaking (4)

22 Governed by chance (6)

23 One making 1 *ac* (6)

DOWN

2 J. B. —, English novelist, playwright (9)

3 Day before an event (3)

4 Junior hospital post (8)

5 Roald —, British writer (4)

6 Mechanism detonating the cartridge in rifle (6,3)

7 Man's name (3)

11 It's worn to hold back the hair (5,4)

13 Song from musical *No, No, Nanette* (3,3,3)

14 Mexican hat (8)

18 Tropical tree (4)

20 Ocean (3)

21 Large extinct New Zealand bird (3)

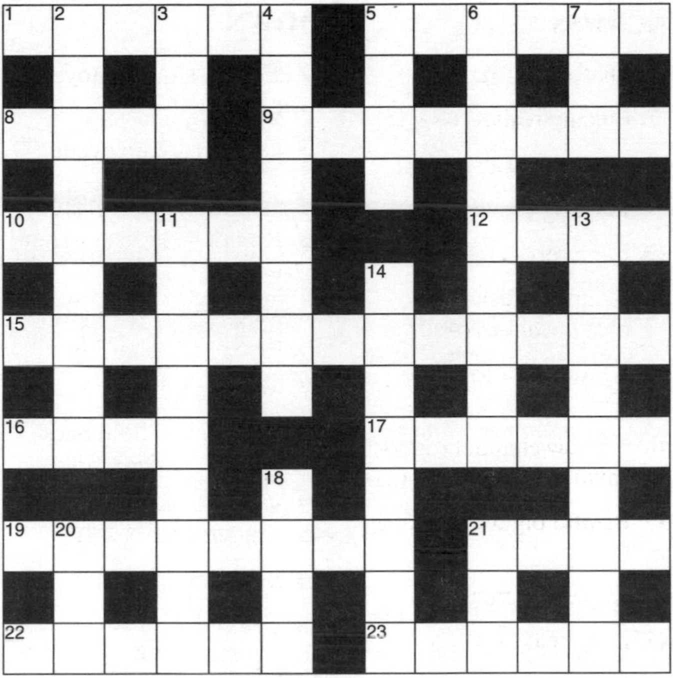
1
2
3
4
5
6
7
8
9
10
11
12
13
14
15
16
17
18
19
20
21
22
23

ACROSS

1 Meal (9)

6 Luggage item; catch (3)

8 Be relevant (5)

9 Partitioned-off part of room (7)

10 Fruit (6)

12 Max —, 20th century German Surrealist artist (5)

13 Cutting implement (6)

14 Hard work; party (6)

17 Knock over (5)

19 German art songs (6)

21 Herbal flavouring (7)

22 Haricots for instance (5)

23 Ovum (3)

24 Develops rapidly (9)

DOWN

1 Defeat; strike (4)

2 Violently shatter (7)

3 Eg, Ctrl, Alt or Esc (3)

4 Secure (in position) (6)

5 Crockery, cutlery, etc (9)

6 Francis —, 20th century Irish artist (5)

7 More important (7)

11 Atmospheric current (9)

13 *Not a* — means nothing (7)

15 Culinary herb (7)

16 — Cooper, English actress (6)

18 Wound (from bee) (5)

20 The Thames at Oxford (4)

22 Prickly seed case (3)

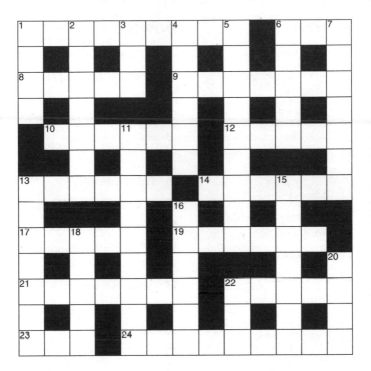

ACROSS

1 Sacred place (7)

5 Small tree bright in autumn (5)

8 Dromedary, perhaps (5)

9 Member of religious and military order (7)

10 South Yorks town (8)

11 Tidy (4)

13 Adopt support role (4,1,4,4)

16 Desert material (4)

17 Occurring every other year (8)

20 Japanese warrior (7)

21 Permission for absence from school (5)

22 Ungracefully tall (5)

23 Lumpy (7)

DOWN

1 Early trombone (7)

2 One giving appellation (5)

3 Magical object (8)

4 Number specialist (13)

5 Identical (4)

6 Type of cross (7)

7 Gold purity measure (5)

12 One with cropped hair (8)

14 Blood relation (7)

15 Early '60s satellite (7)

16 Fibre-yielding agave (5)

18 Perfect (5)

19 Flat carrier (4)

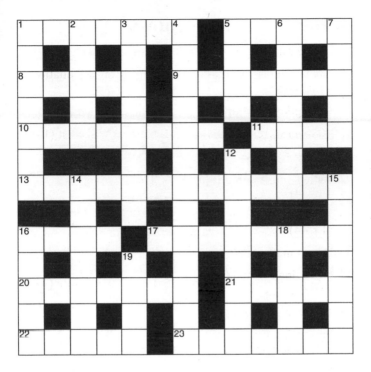

ACROSS

1 Imploring (7)

5 Abolish; cut of meat (4)

9 Forcibly pull (something from someone's grip) (5)

10 Pleasurable inactivity (7)

11 A.M. in full (4,8)

12 Tented entertainment (6)

13 Ocean floor (6)

16 System of names (12)

19 Family name of tsars (7)

20 City of Nebraska (5)

21 (Of ship) lean (4)

22 Search haphazardly (7)

DOWN

1 Deep dish (4)

2 Leftover grain gatherer (7)

3 Competing with a fair chance of success (2,3,7)

4 Aureate (6)

6 Beautiful young woman (5)

7 Egyptian monument (7)

8 Temporary police set-up near site of crime (8,4)

12 Near the middle (7)

14 *Major —*, play by Shaw (7)

15 Wading bird (6)

17 Viral disease mainly affecting children (5)

18 Period of lower prices (4)

ACROSS

1 Sequence (6)

4 Made great efforts (6)

8 Romantic feeling (4)

9 Have different opinions (8)

10 HP description (4,5)

13 What may be measured in watts (5)

15 Friend (*Spanish*) (5)

16 Female name (5)

18 General agreement (9)

21 Administrative district of country (8)

22 Large piece of stone (4)

23 Thick soup (6)

24 More close (6)

DOWN

1 Vendor (6)

2 Cramming (for exam) (8)

3 Grass-like plant (5)

5 Put (music) into a different key (9)

6 Yours and mine (4)

7 Devon city (6)

11 Roofing with straw or reeds (9)

12 Rule as monarch (5)

14 One fighting in ring (8)

16 Leap in the air (4,2)

17 Weather map line (6)

19 Earthenware beer jug (5)

20 Mislaid (4)

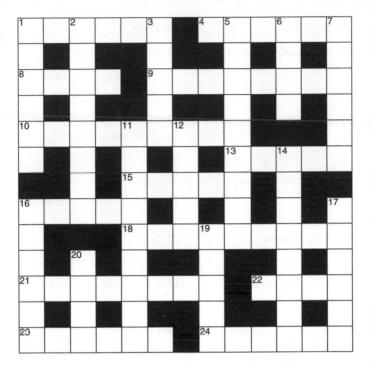

ACROSS

1 Judgement; settlement (8)

5 Long poem (4)

9 Unchanging in a particular belief (4,2,3,4)

10 Retain (4)

11 Eg, beef (3,4)

13 Soak up (6)

15 Carved figure (6)

18 Noble's rank or dignity (7)

20 Units (4)

23 (Of ship) returning to port of origin (8-5)

24 Routes; styles (4)

25 Acting out a part (4,4)

DOWN

1 Extinct bird (4)

2 Large island in the Mediterranean (5)

3 Captain; butterfly (7)

4 Expression of strong public disapproval (6)

6 Throw out; school work (7)

7 Knee-length trousers (8)

8 Source of river (4)

12 Common TV format (4,4)

14 Rough cider (7)

16 Difficulty, problems (7)

17 Stage in development of unborn child (6)

19 Consume (drink); sad (4)

21 Match, rival (5)

22 Small whirlpool (4)

ACROSS

5 Wall recess (6)

7 *Persuasion* author (6)

9 Molière's hypocrite (8)

11 Wise; herb (4)

12 Undergrowth; fox tail (5)

13 Ankara its capital (6)

15 Reprimand; rug (6)

17 Reptile (5)

19 Part of plant or hair (4)

20 Antlered creature (8)

22 A constituent of water (6)

23 Tightly grasp; eggs (6)

DOWN

1 Abbreviation for Cambridge University (6)

2 Feudal labourer (4)

3 Rich cake (6)

4 Leg joint (4)

6 Going round and round (11)

8 Holiday seller (6,5)

10 Not cool (5)

14 Gone up (5)

16 Task involving short journey (6)

18 Suggestive of soil (6)

19 Crowd disturbance (4)

21 2.54 cm (4)

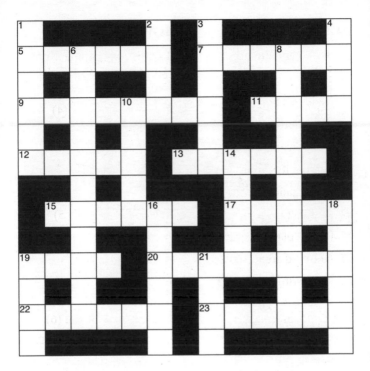

ACROSS

1 With parts the other way round (4,5)

6 Distress call (3)

8 Bike rider (7)

9 Spiteful (5)

10 Very small amount (4)

11 Widespread respect for high quality (8)

13 One leaving their nation (6)

14 Extremely sad (6)

17 Domestic drink (3,5)

18 Courageous man (4)

20 Direction of Edinburgh from Cardiff (5)

21 Bandit (7)

22 Pig pen (3)

23 Controller (9)

DOWN

1 Immunity provider (7)

2 Drinks do (8,5)

3 Useless; conceited (4)

4 Hold back (6)

5 Lineage (8)

6 One occupying property when it is sold (7,6)

7 Manner; elegance (5)

12 Pause for rest (8)

15 Seafood soup (7)

16 Cuppa maker (3,3)

17 Curling —; sugar — (5)

19 High land (4)

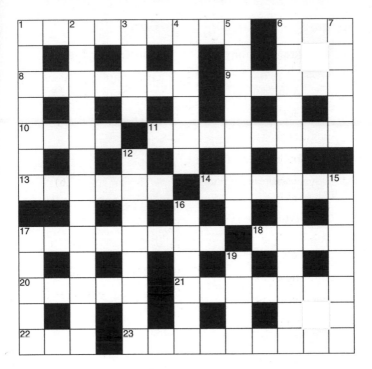

ACROSS

1 Joined by stitching (4)

3 Neglected (7)

8 Latin for Wales (7)

9 An order of classical architecture (5)

10 Group of nine (5)

11 Professional entertainer (7)

13 Came into a title (9)

17 Spray can (7)

19 Move slowly (5)

20 First prime minister of India (5)

22 Filmed on tape (7)

23 Yellow element (7)

24 Coloured eye part (4)

DOWN

1 1/86400 of a day (6)

2 Man amorously pursuing females (9)

3 Discreetly conceal (4,1,4,4)

4 Holy man (5)

5 Male descendant (3)

6 Port worker (6)

7 Theatre reviewer (6)

12 1685 battle ending Monmouth's rebellion (9)

14 Resolve, settle (6)

15 — Wallis, British engineer (*World War II bouncing bombs*) (6)

16 Suit; tools (6)

18 Cardinal point (5)

21 Falstaff's prince (3)

ACROSS

1 Remove (from case) (6)

7 Continent (6)

8 Laboratory item (4,4)

10 Put in fetters (7)

11 Small hard swelling (7)

12 Proverb (5)

14 Restoration to health after, eg, addiction (*informal*) (5)

15 Brilliant effect (5)

19 Paper token (7)

20 Small paddled boat (7)

22 Teach (8)

23 Hazel flower spike (6)

24 Main traffic route (6)

DOWN

1 Ability to understand something (6)

2 Of country life (8)

3 7th century Northumbrian saint (8)

4 Eager; wail (4)

5 Curved up in the centre (6)

6 Leap; well (6)

9 Ludwig van — (9)

12 One removing by force (8)

13 European nobleman (8)

16 Sung by a choir (6)

17 Northernmost US state (6)

18 Delicately attractive (6)

21 Join (4)

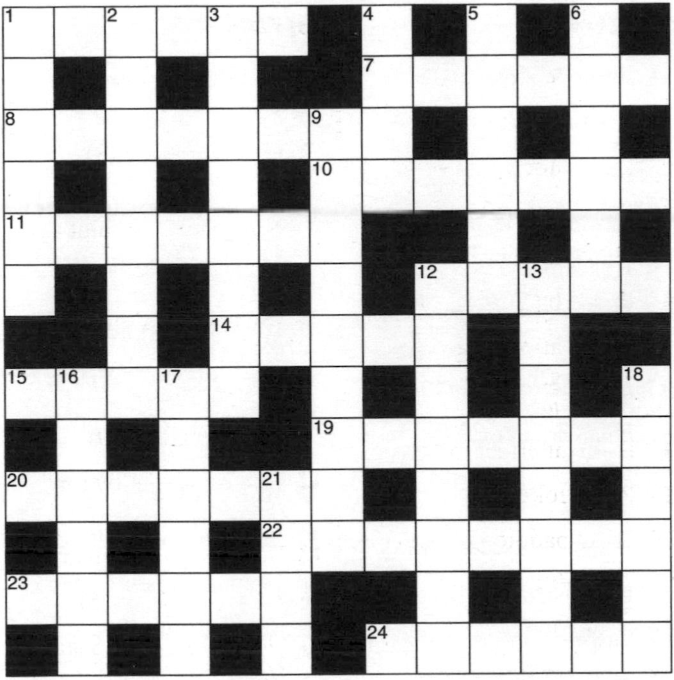
1
2
3
4
5
6
7
8
9
10
11
12
13
14
15
16
17
18
19
20
21
22
23
24

ACROSS

1 Secret clique (5)

4 (Three) sister goddesses famed for their beauty (6)

8 Aromatic herb (8)

9 Bucket (4)

10 Dull routine behaviour (3)

11 Earnest request (8)

14 Nuns' leader (6)

16 Expression of wild delight (6)

18 Machinery repairer (8)

20 Long period of time (3)

21 Surprise police visit (4)

22 Unskilled worker (8)

23 Afternoon nap (6)

24 Come in (5)

DOWN

1 Geological period (8)

2 Garden feeder (4,5)

3 Large cat (7)

5 Wed again (7)

6 Drink of tea (*informal*) (5)

7 (Of flavours) hot (5)

12 Highly confidential (3,6)

13 One who makes good damage (8)

15 Brilliant red (7)

17 Shut in (*rare spelling*) (7)

18 Financial resources (5)

19 Small group of people trained for a purpose (5)

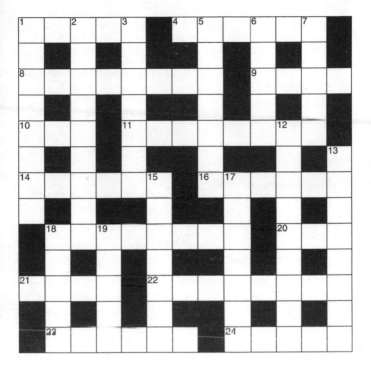

ACROSS

6 1952 Western film (*Gary Cooper*) (4,4)

8 His sons were Shem, Ham and Japheth (4)

9 German World War II prison camp (6)

10 Mocking remark (5)

11 The defeating of a more powerful opponent (5-7)

12 Alice went through it (7,5)

15 All together (*music*) (5)

16 Rectangular (6)

18 Former Indian coin; girl (4)

19 *You're a better man than I am, — — ! (Kipling)* (5,3)

DOWN

1 Covered with gold (4)

2 The muse of comedy (6)

3 In existence for years (4-8)

4 (Of plant) living for a year or less (6)

5 1066 battle (8)

7 There is no prospect of agreement (*informal*) (7,5)

11 Appearance of a secondary image on a screen (8)

13 Canvas carrier for soldier's possessions (6)

14 Lasting 24 hours (3-3)

17 Detect or catch (a criminal) (*informal*) (4)

ACROSS

1 Type of envelope for return at no cost (5-4)

7 Body of Zulu warriors (4)

8 (Light-brown) sugar (8)

9 Stay (6)

10 Member of Andean people conquered by Spain (4)

12 One composing or solving chess conundrums (10)

13 *The — —* denotes London's financial area (6,4)

16 Stout cord (4)

17 Scott —, US ragtime composer (6)

18 Walked aimlessly (8)

20 Expel (4)

21 Sincerely and seriously (9)

DOWN

1 Bitterly regretting (*longer spelling*) (6)

2 Artist such as Millais (3-10)

3 Archaic affirmative (3)

4 Large-flowered bulb (9)

5 The cutting off of limbs (13)

6 Science of vision (6)

11 1950-3 conflict (6,3)

14 Minimum number needed to take decisions (6)

15 Fast (6)

19 Nickname of Aneurin Bevan (3)

ACROSS

1 Ottorino —, Italian composer (*The Pines of Rome*) (8)

5 Wild pig (4)

8 Not young (3)

9 See; round mark (4)

10 (Of seeds) planted (4)

12 Keep on to the end (4,3,6)

13 Church song book (6)

14 Real or lawn game (6)

17 Disgusting quality (13)

20 At what time (4)

21 Farm animals (4)

22 Knowing; insect (3)

23 Pay attention to; tone (4)

24 Senior Service colour (4,4)

DOWN

1 Sources; rummages (5)

2 Throwing manner (7)

3 Having desires impossible to satisfy (10)

4 Horny parts of horse (6)

6 Smell (5)

7 (Park) keepers (7)

11 In an incompetent manner (10)

13 Gained with difficulty (4-3)

15 Requisite, necessary (7)

16 Sandstone constituent (6)

18 Stitched fold (5)

19 Distinctive arrangement; elegance (5)

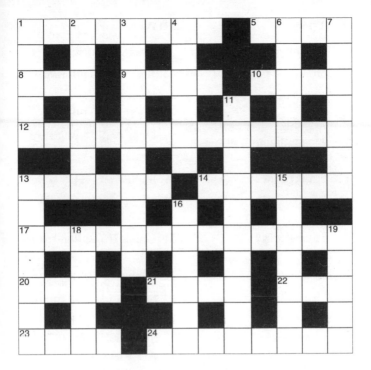

ACROSS

1 Determined courage (5)

4 Impressive boldness (7)

8 Spice from crocus (7)

9 Pulsate (5)

10 One not fighting in war (3-9)

12 (Drink) container (6)

13 Courage in battle (6)

16 Production of molecules in living cells (12)

18 Preliminary section (of music) (*informal*) (5)

20 It hangs outside pub (3,4)

22 Outstanding courage (7)

23 Sensation transmitter (5)

DOWN

1 Infected matter (3)

2 Bold, frank (*informal*) (7)

3 Sea port in Fife (9)

4 Deprive of feeling (6)

5 Skill (3)

6 Main artery (5)

7 Non-landing spacecraft (7)

11 Greek Trojan War leader (9)

12 Immature (7)

14 Sir Laurence —, English actor (*Hamlet, 1948*) (7)

15 Central hall or court (6)

17 External (5)

19 Kimono sash (3)

21 Scots form of no (3)

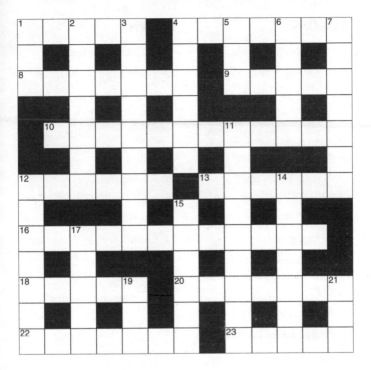

times2 Crossword

ACROSS

1 Not great (in number) (5)

7 Alongside (7)

8 Pickled herring fillet (7)

9 Group of assistants (7)

10 Site of dam on the Nile (5)

11 Large artillery pieces (7)

13 Seasickness is — *de mer* (3)

15 (Of food) spicy (3)

17 Turned to new purpose (7)

19 Modern witchcraft (5)

21 Italian radio pioneer (7)

23 County (7)

24 In operation (7)

25 One giving something (5)

DOWN

1 Mocking irony (7)

2 Permit (5)

3 Spanish region associated with Don Quixote (2,6)

4 Courage; small stones (4)

5 Decorate, embellish (7)

6 Determination; metal (5)

7 Tie for kitchen wear (5,6)

12 Quaint (3-5)

14 Primitive toilet (7)

16 Rod in organ mechanism; trailer (7)

18 Smug smile (5)

20 Act comically (5)

22 US state (4)

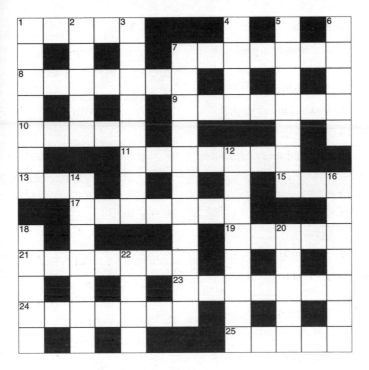

ACROSS

1 (Of mouth) wide open (6)

4 Reaper's tool (6)

9 Zodiac sign (7)

10 Fool (5)

11 Page of postage stamps (5)

13 Fern (7)

14 Swan; loaf (3)

15 Made holy (*archaic*) (5)

16 Lowest cardinal number (3)

17 Officially examine (7)

19 One dealing dishonestly (5)

21 Italian city near Venice (5)

22 Open-meshed material (7)

24 Indicate, signify (6)

25 Offer for sale; demand (6)

DOWN

1 Eg, O, H, Ne, CO, etc (5)

2 Generally true saying (7)

3 Pinch, bite (3)

5 Coming to exciting peak (9)

6 Use one's mind (5)

7 Friendly understanding (7)

8 Part of old road surface (11)

12 Seasoning for meal (5,4)

14 Fastened; shorn (7)

16 Tapering stone pillar (7)

18 Carried chair (5)

20 Drunk; firm; concise (5)

23 Meal; drink (3)

ACROSS

1 Qualification (indicating a person's suitability) (10)

7 Subatomic particle (7)

8 Imprecise (in thought) (5)

10 Keep in subjection (7)

11 Object surviving from earlier times (5)

12 Make cuts in (surface) (6)

15 Bringer of good luck (6)

17 Upper chambers of the heart (5)

18 Bewitch (7)

21 North African country (5)

22 Chief port of Sicily (7)

23 Woven together (10)

DOWN

1 Small group (of trees) (5)

2 Strange, frightening (5)

3 — Hemingway; — Shackleton (6)

4 Greek restaurant (7)

5 Seraphic (7)

6 Make drunk (10)

9 The production of a higher state of energy (10)

13 A fuss (*informal*) (5-2)

14 Alarm (someone) (7)

16 Friendly correspondent (3,3)

19 Abdominal pain (5)

20 Unpleasantly bitter (5)

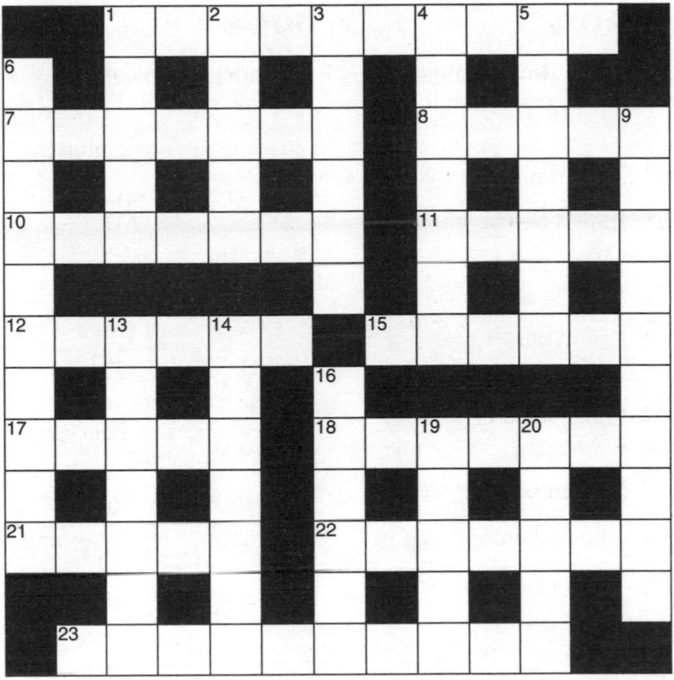
1 2 3 4 5
6
7 8 9
10 11
12 13 14 15
16
17 18 19 20
21 22
23

ACROSS

1 Unvarying; clothing (7)

5 Eg, outlet of the Nile (5)

8 Awkward, clumsy (5)

9 Ability to sustain effort (7)

10 Extension to match (5,4)

12 *To — out* is to make last (3)

13 Canadian province (6)

14 Winner (6)

17 Grow older (3)

18 Bird discourager (9)

20 Reduced in thickness (7)

21 Merry, squiffy (5)

23 Argentinian dance (5)

24 Cocaine (*informal*); fool (*informal*) (7)

DOWN

1 Come together (5)

2 Decorate (cake) (3)

3 Scots biscuit (7)

4 Cotton cloth (6)

5 Arrange (cloth) loosely (5)

6 City; Robert Dudley (9)

7 Non professional; 8 *ac* (7)

11 Shortly after that (9)

13 Group of four (7)

15 Tendency to do nothing (7)

16 Like an ancient poet (6)

18 Powered control mechanism (5)

19 Bruce — was Batman (5)

22 Mate (3)

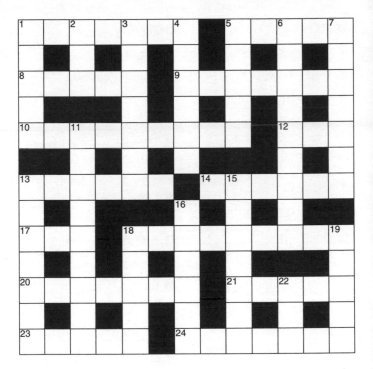

ACROSS

3 Braying animal (3)

8 Teach; retinue (5)

9 Mark out in coloured squares (7)

10 Henry —, 17th century English composer (*Dido and Aeneas*) (7)

11 Native to Berne (5)

12 Period holding office (6)

14 Soup dish (6)

15 Adjust (eg, piano) again (6)

17 Gender; make ineffective (6)

20 Arm of the sea (5)

21 Official investigation (7)

24 Not exactly matched (7)

25 Embedded decoration (5)

26 Venomous snake (3)

DOWN

1 Pace (4)

2 Regular customer (6)

3 Fourth wife of Henry VIII (4)

4 Angrily rebuke (5)

5 Allay fears of (someone) (8)

6 Lying face upwards (6)

7 One in gaol (8)

12 End (of rail line) (8)

13 Sound genuine (4,4)

16 Inclined (6)

18 Thing of little value (6)

19 Stringed instrument (5)

22 Witty remark (4)

23 Child's toy (2-2)

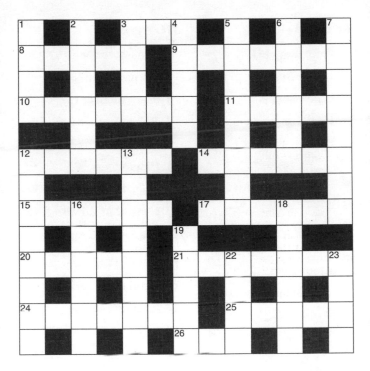

ACROSS

7 Once more (5)

8 Before first light (7)

9 Fellow soldier (7)

10 Cuttlefish pigment (5)

11 Peter — Rubens, Flemish painter (4)

12 Brae (8)

15 African nation (8)

16 Long heroic story (4)

19 Fine cotton thread (5)

21 Minor illness (7)

22 Stiff; like potatoes (7)

23 Form of lily (5)

DOWN

1 Foolish, reckless (6)

2 Cornish town (8)

3 Work (dough) (5)

4 Relating to tension (7)

5 Plucked instrument (4)

6 Employ, hire (6)

8 Done in preparation (11)

13 Consort of Edward II (8)

14 Eugène —, French dramatist (*Theatre of the Absurd*) (7)

15 Enrol in the services (6)

17 Existing, real (6)

18 Like clubs and spades (5)

20 George Bernard —, Irish dramatist (4)

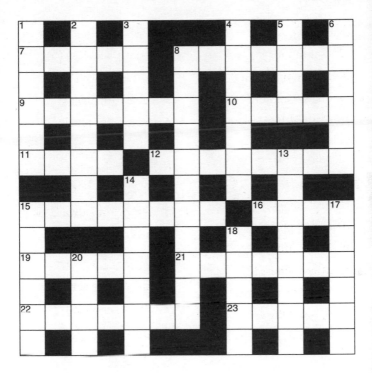

The Solutions

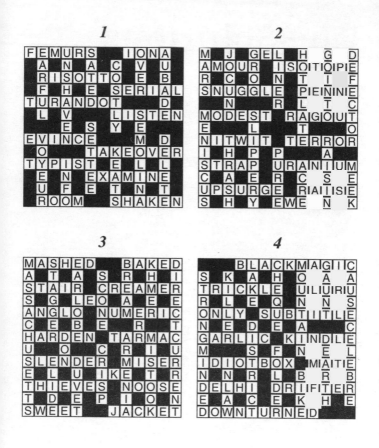

1

```
F E M U R S   ■ ■ I O N A
■ A ■ N ■ A ■ C ■ V ■ U ■ R
■ R I S O T T O ■ E ■ B ■
■ F ■ H ■ E ■ S E R I A L
T U R A N D O T ■ ■ D ■ ■
■ L ■ V ■ ■ L I S T E N ■
■ ■ E ■ S ■ Y ■ E ■ ■ ■
E V I N C E ■ ■ M ■ D ■
■ O ■ ■ T A K E O V E R
T Y P I S T ■ E ■ L ■ L ■
■ E ■ N ■ E X A M I N E ■
■ U ■ F ■ E ■ ■ T ■ N ■ T
R O O M ■ ■ S H A K E N
```

2

```
M ■ J ■ G E L ■ H ■ G ■ D
A M O U R ■ I S O T O P E
R ■ C ■ O N ■ T ■ I ■ F ■
S N U G G L E ■ P E N N I E
■ N ■ ■ R ■ L ■ T ■ C ■
M O D E S T ■ R A G O U T
E ■ L ■ ■ T ■ ■ T ■ ■ O
N I T W I T ■ T E R R O R
I ■ H ■ P ■ P ■ ■ A ■
S T R A P ■ U R A N I U M
C ■ A ■ E ■ R ■ C ■ S ■ E
U P S U R G E ■ R A I S E
S ■ H ■ Y ■ E W E ■ ■ N ■ K
```

3

```
M A S H E D ■ ■ B A K E D
A ■ T ■ A ■ S ■ R ■ H ■ I
S T A I R ■ C R E A M E R
S ■ G ■ L E O ■ A ■ E ■ E
A N G L O ■ N U M E R I C
C ■ E ■ B ■ E ■ R ■ ■ T
H A R D E N ■ T A R M A C
U ■ O ■ ■ C ■ R ■ I ■ U
S L E N D E R ■ M I S E R
E ■ L ■ I K E ■ T ■ R ■
T H I E V E S ■ N O O S E
T ■ D ■ E ■ P ■ I ■ O ■ N
S W E E T ■ ■ J A C K E T
```

4

```
■ ■ B L A C K M A G I C
S ■ K ■ A ■ H ■ O ■ A ■ A
T R I C K L E ■ U L U R U
R ■ L ■ E ■ Q ■ N ■ N ■ S
O N L Y ■ S U B T I T L E
N ■ E ■ D ■ E ■ A ■ ■ C
G A R L I C ■ K I N D L E
M ■ ■ S ■ F ■ N ■ E ■ L
I D I O T B O X ■ M A T E
N ■ N ■ R ■ L ■ B ■ R ■ B
D E L H I ■ D R I F T E R
E ■ A ■ C ■ E ■ K ■ H ■ E
D O W N T U R N E D ■ ■
```

5

S	T	O	M	A	C	H			B	O	W	L
	U		O		I		H		A		E	
P	R	O	P	E	R		U	P	R	O	A	R
	B				C		M		O		P	
D	O	O	R	J	A	M	B		M	O	O	D
	T		O				U		E		N	
		O	B	B	L	I	G	A	T	O		
	P		I		I			E		B		
P	E	O	N		M	U	S	H	R	O	O	M
	T		H		P		C			G		
B	R	O	O	K	E		A	L	M	O	N	D
	O		O		T		L		A		O	
C	L	O	D			N	E	W	Y	O	R	K

6

P	R	O	S	A	I	C		C	A	T	C	H
O		W		R		U		A		O		E
L	A	N	C	E		R	E	S	P	O	N	D
E		E			A		T		M		G	
C	U	R		F	O	R	T	I	T	U	D	E
A			A		E		G		C			
T	U	B	I	N	G		F	A	T	H	O	M
		L		A		C		T			A	
F	R	U	S	T	R	A	T	E		C	A	N
A		F		I		N		R		R		D
D	E	F	A	C	T	O		O	M	E	G	A
E		E		A		V		V		D		T
R	U	R	A	L		A	B	A	L	O	N	E

7

S	H	O	W	B	O	A	T		A	D	A	M
L		C		A		T		D		E		E
A	L	C	O	H	O	L		O	S	I	E	R
P		U		A		A		R		C		C
	P	R	A	M		S	T	Y	L	I	S	H
P			A		T			D		A		
I	N	M	O	S	T		A	S	T	E	R	N
N		I		S		C		C				T
A	C	R	O	B	A	T		H	U	L	K	
F		A		A		E		E		B		
O	S	C	A	R		T	E	R	E	N	C	E
R		L		K		I		Z		I		E
E	Y	E	S		S	C	H	O	O	N	E	R

8

D	A	T	U	M		B		O		H		
A		O		U		R	E	P	R	O	O	F
V	E	R	B	E	N	A		P		G		
I		Q		S		E	G	G	H	E	A	D
D	O	U	B	L	E		A		A		R	
	E		I	N	D	E	M	N	I	T	Y	
P			C		L			H				
P	A	N	O	R	A	M	I	C		R		
	R		U		S		C	A	M	E	R	A
C	L	O	T	T	E	D		N		C		T
	O		G			O	W	N	G	O	A	L
Q	U	E	U	I	N	G		E		I		A
	R		N			E		S	O	L	E	S

9

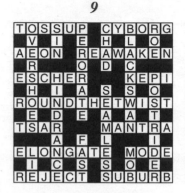

10

11

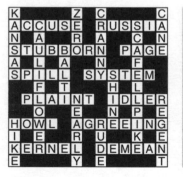

12

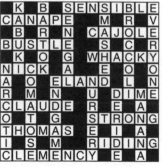

13

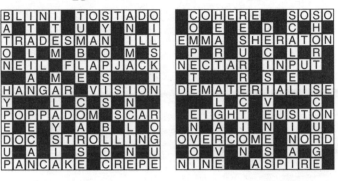

| | | | | | | | | | | | | |
|B|L|I|N|I| |T|O|S|T|A|D|O|
|A| |T| |T| |U| |Y| |N| |I|
|T|R|A|D|E|S|M|A|N| |I|L|L|
|O| |L| |M| |B| |O| |M| |S|
N	E	I	L		F	L	A	P	J	A	C	K
		A		M		E		S				I
H	A	N	G	A	R		V	I	S	I	O	N
Y			L		C		S		N			
P	O	P	P	A	D	O	M		S	C	A	R
E		E		Y		A		B		L		O
D	O	C		S	T	R	O	L	L	I	N	G
U		A		I		S		O		N		U
P	A	N	C	A	K	E		C	R	E	P	E

14

C	O	H	E	R	E			S	O	S	O
O		E		E		D		C		H	
E	M	M	A		S	H	E	R	A	T	O	N
	P		R		U		C		L		R	
N	E	C	T	A	R		I	N	P	U	T	
	T			R			S		E			
D	E	M	A	T	E	R	I	A	L	I	S	E
		L		C		V			C			
E	I	G	H	T		E	U	S	T	O	N	
N		A		I		N		I		U		
O	V	E	R	C	O	M	E		N	O	R	D
O		V		N		S		A		G		
N	I	N	E		A	S	P	I	R	E

15

J	A	L	A	P	E	N	O		P	R	O
M		R		X		P		L		R	
B	L	I	T	H	E	S	P	I	R	I	T
L		A		I			E		N		
H	E	L	D		B	A	C	K	D	R	O	P
	N		I		A			C			
M	O	L	E	S	T		M	A	R	R	O	W
K			O		F		A				
K	I	L	O	G	R	A	M		P	R	A	Y
N		B		B		T		N			
S	A	L	E	O	R	R	E	T	U	R	N
W		S		U		R		R		I	
A	L	E		B	A	T	T	E	R	E	D

16

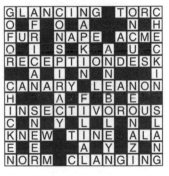

G	L	A	N	C	I	N	G		T	O	R	C
O		F		O		A			N		H	
F	U	R		N	A	P	E		A	C	M	E
O		I		S		K		A		U		C
R	E	C	E	P	T	I	O	N	D	E	S	K
A		A		I		N		N			I	
C	A	N	A	R	Y		L	E	A	N	O	N
H			A		F		B		E			
I	N	S	E	C	T	I	V	O	R	O	U	S
C		N		Y		L		L		N		L
K	N	E	W		T	I	N	E		A	L	A
E		E		A		Y		Z		N		
N	O	R	M		C	L	A	N	G	I	N	G

17

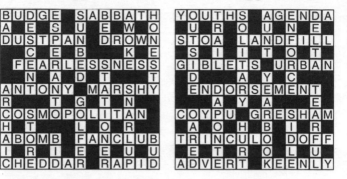

B	U	D	G	E		S	A	B	B	A	T	H
A		E	S		U		E		W		O	
D	U	S	T	P	A	N		D	R	O	W	N
		C		E		B		K			E	
	F	E	A	R	L	E	S	S	N	E	S	S
	N		A		D		T				T	
A	N	T	O	N	Y		M	A	R	S	H	Y
R		T		G		T		N				
C	O	S	M	O	P	O	L	I	T	A	N	
H		T		L		O		R				
A	B	O	M	B		F	A	N	C	L	U	B
I		R		I		E		E		U		
C	H	E	D	D	A	R		R	A	P	I	D

18

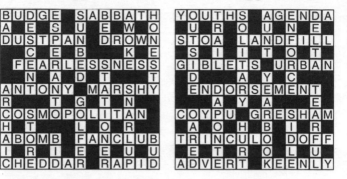

Y	O	U	T	H	S		A	G	E	N	D	A
	U		R		O		U		N		E	
S	T	O	A		L	A	N	D	F	I	L	L
	S		I		I		T		O		T	
G	I	B	L	E	T	S		U	R	B	A	N
	D				A		Y		C			
	E	N	D	O	R	S	E	M	E	N	T	
		A			Y		A				E	
C	O	Y	P	U		G	R	E	S	H	A	M
	A		O		H		B		I		R	
T	R	I	N	C	U	L	O		D	O	F	F
	E				R		L		U			
A	D	V	E	R	T		K	E	E	N	L	Y

19

T	W	I	T		D	O	W	N	W	I	N	D
	E		W		A		A		A		E	
R	E	V	I	E	W	E	R		G	O	W	N
	D		S		N		B		E		G	
W	Y	A	T	T		F	L	Y	S	W	A	T
A		E		M		I			T			
S	W	E	R	V	E		N	E	P	H	E	W
	A			N		G		R			E	
P	L	Y	W	O	O	D		W	O	R	S	T
	L		I		F		W		W		W	
W	O	R	D		W	H	A	T	E	V	E	R
	O		O		A		S		S		D	
S	N	O	W	D	R	O	P		S	K	E	W

20

B	I	S	E	C	T			S	C	U	D	
U		U		H		I		C		L		U
C	A	R	V	E		M	A	R	V	E	L	L
K		F		A		P		E		A		C
S	H	A	M	P	O	O		D	U	N	C	E
		C				R		I				T
	P	E	R	M	U	T	A	T	I	O	N	
P				U		U					P	
H	E	A	P	S		N	E	W	P	O	R	T
Y		L		S		A		I		S		H
S	O	O	N	E	S	T		P	U	S	S	Y
I		N		L		E		E		U		M
O	B	E	Y			G	R	A	M	M	E	

21

22

23

24

25

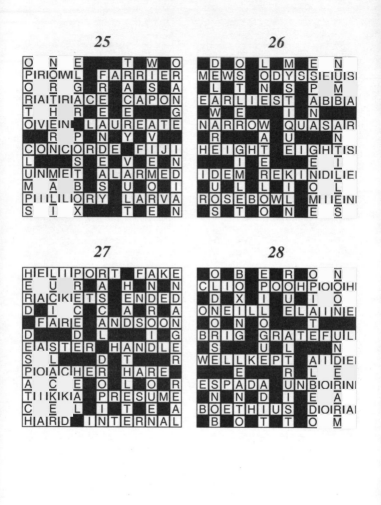

26

27

28

29

30

31

32

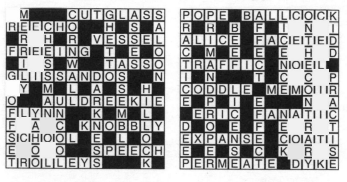

33

34

35

36

37

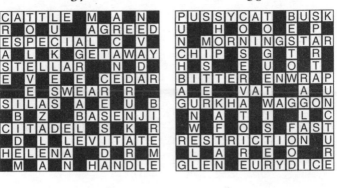

38

39

40

41

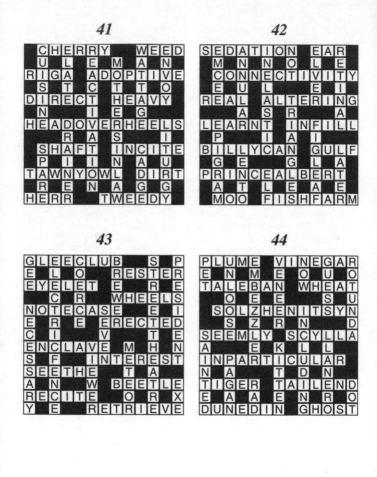

42

43

44

45

```
C I V I C . . J . M . L
O . I . L . P R O F I L E
R I V I E R A . H . N . V
O . A . A . L I N K A G E
N O T O N . I . . R . L .
. . . C O N D O N E . . .
T O G . U . D . V . T I C
. . A S T A R T E . . . A
M . L . O . R E F E R . .
A N A G R A M . B . A . P
D . H . O . E X O T I C A
A T A L O S S . O . R . R
M . D . F . . K A Y A K .
```

46

```
. E M P L O Y M E N T . .
P . N . H . F . R . I . .
O D D L Y . F I S H N E T
S . E . S . I . J . O . .
T I M . I N C E S S A N T
M . I . C . E . P . . . H
O R C H I D . B A N G L E
R . . . S . P . G . O . P
T W E N T I E T H . W H O
E . I . . N . E . R . I .
M I D D L E C . T H O R N
E . I . . I . T . N . T .
P R O P E L L I N G . . .
```

47

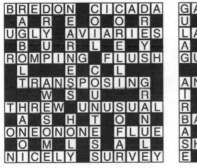

```
B R E D O N . C I C A D A
A . R . E . O . O . R . .
U G L Y . A V I A R I E S
. B . U . R . L . E . Y .
R O M P I N G . F L U S H
. L . E . C . L . . . . .
. T R A N S P O S I N G .
. W . S . U . . . . . R .
T H R E W . U N U S U A L
A . S . H . T . O . N . .
O N E O N O N E . F L U E
. O . M . L . S . A . L .
N I C E L Y . S U R V E Y
```

48

```
G A D A R E N E . F . N .
U . Y . O . A . T R I P E
L A N C A S T E R . E . W
A . A . N . I . A . N A Y
G U S T . A V O W E D . E
. T . M . E . L . . . . A
A N Y H O W . H E C T O R
I . . . I . G . R . O . .
R . G U S T A V . O W E D
B A R . T . N . M . R . I
A . E . E N D E A V O U R
S H E E N . H . R . P . G
E . T . . M I S E R E R E
```

49

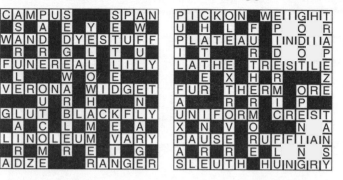

```
C A M P U S     S P A N
  S   A   E Y E   W
W A N D   D Y E S T U F F
  R   R   G   L   T   U
F U N E R E A L   L I L Y
  L     W   O   E
V E R O N A   W I D G E T
      U   R   H     N
G L U T   B L A C K F L Y
    A   C   L   M   E A
L I N O L E U M   V A R Y
  R   M   R   E   I   G
A D Z E     R A N G E R
```

50

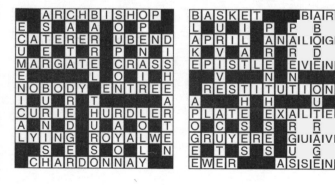

```
P I C K O N   W E I G H T
U   H   L   F   P   O   R
P L A T E A U   I N D I A
I   T     R   D   O   P
L A T H E   T R E S T L E
    E   X   H   R     Z
F U R   T H E R M   O R E
A     R   R   I   P
U N I F O R M   C R E S T
X   N   V   O     N   A
P A U S E   R U F F I A N
A   R   R   E   L   N   S
S L E U T H   H U N G R Y
```

51

```
  A R C H B I S H O P
E   S   A   A   O   P
C A T E R E R   U B E N D
U   E   T   R   P   N   I
M A R G A T E   C R A S S
E       L   O   I   H
N O B O D Y   E N T R E E
I   U   R   T       A
C U R I E   H U R D L E R
A   N   D   U   A   O   T
L Y I N G   R O Y A L W E
  S   E   S   O   L   N
  C H A R D O N N A Y
```

52

```
B A S K E T   B A R B
L   U   I   P   P   B O
A P R I L   A N A L O G Y
K   V   A   R   R   D   I
E P I S T L E   E V E N S
    V   N   N     N   H
  R E S T I T U T I O N
A   H   H   U
P L A T E   E X A L T E D
O   C   S   R   R   E
G R U Y E R E   G U A V A
E   T   S   U   G   L
E W E R     A S S E N T
```

53

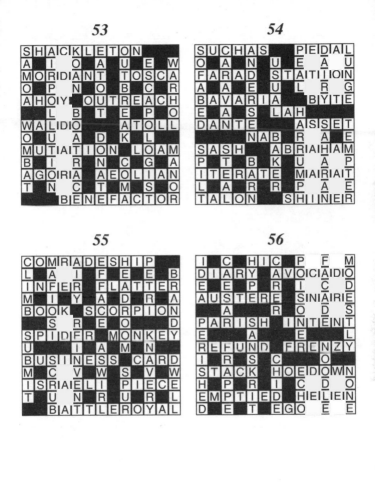

54

55

56

57

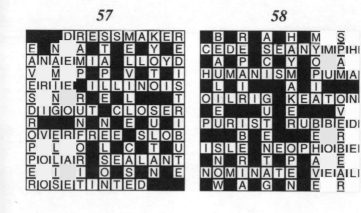

58

59

60

61

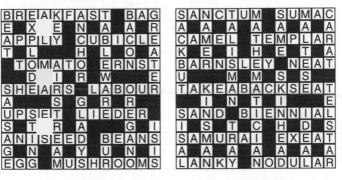

B	R	E	A	K	F	A	S	T		B	A	G
E		X		E		N		A		A		R
A	P	P	L	Y		C	U	B	I	C	L	E
T		L		H		L		O		A		
	T	O	M	A	T	O		E	R	N	S	T
	D		I		R		W			E		
S	H	E	A	R	S		L	A	B	O	U	R
A			S		G		R		R			
U	P	S	E	T		L	I	E	D	E	R	
S		T		R		A		G			I	
A	N	I	S	E	E	D		B	E	A	N	S
G		N		A		Y		U		N		I
E	G	G		M	U	S	H	R	O	O	M	S

62

S	A	N	C	T	U	M		S	U	M	A	C
A		A		A		A		A		A		A
C	A	M	E	L		T	E	M	P	L	A	R
K		E		I		H		E		T		A
B	A	R	N	S	L	E	Y		N	E	A	T
U				M		M		S		S		
T	A	K	E	A	B	A	C	K	S	E	A	T
	I		N		T		I			E		
S	A	N	D		B	I	E	N	N	I	A	L
I		S		T		C		H		D		S
S	A	M	U	R	A	I		E	X	E	A	T
A		A		A		A		A		A		A
L	A	N	K	Y		N	O	D	U	L	A	R

63

B	E	G	G	I	N	G			C	H	O	P
O		L		N		O		I		O		Y
W	R	E	S	T		L	A	N	G	U	O	R
L		A		H		D		C		R		A
	A	N	T	E	M	E	R	I	D	I	E	M
		E		R		N		D			I	
C	I	R	C	U	S		S	E	A	B	E	D
E			N		P		N		A			
N	O	M	E	N	C	L	A	T	U	R	E	
T		U		I		O		R	B		S	
R	O	M	A	N	O	V		O	M	A	H	A
A		P		G		E		O		R		L
L	I	S	T			R	U	M	M	A	G	E

64

S	E	R	I	E	S		S	T	R	O	V	E
E		E		E			R		U		X	
L	O	V	E		D	I	S	A	G	R	E	E
L		I		G		N		S		T		
E	A	S	Y	T	E	R	M	S		E		
R		I		H		E		P	O	W	E	R
	O		A	M	I	G	O			R		
J	A	N	E	T		G		S		E		I
U				C	O	N	S	E	N	S	U	S
M		L		H		T		T				O
P	R	O	V	I	N	C	E		S	L	A	B
U		S		N		I		E		E		A
P	O	T	A	G	E		N	E	A	R	E	R

65

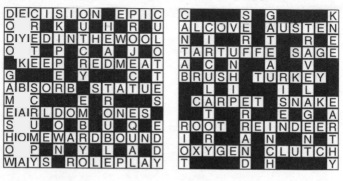

66

67

68

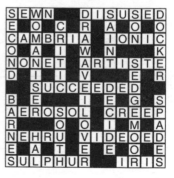

69

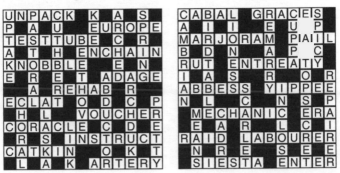

U	N	P	A	C	K		K		A		S	
P		A		U		E	U	R	O	P	E	
T	E	S	T	T	U	B	E		C		R	
A		T		H		E	N	C	H	A	I	N
K	N	O	B	B	L	E		E		N		
E		R		E	T		A	D	A	G	E	
	A		R	E	H	A	B		R			
E	C	L	A	T		O		D	C		P	
	H		L		V	O	U	C	H	E	R	
C	O	R	A	C	L	E		C		D	E	
	R		S		I	N	S	T	R	U	C	T
C	A	T	K	I	N			O		K		T
	L		A		K		A	R	T	E	R	Y

70

C	A	B	A	L		G	R	A	C	E	S
A		I		I		E		U		P	
M	A	R	J	O	R	A	M		P	I	L
B		D		N		A		P		C	
R	U	T		E	N	T	R	E	A	T	Y
I		A		S		R		O		R	
A	B	B	E	S	S		Y	I	P	P	E
N		L		C		N		S		P	
	M	E	C	H	A	N	I	C		E	R
	E		A	R		L		C		I	
R	A	I	D		L	A	B	O	U	R	E
	N		R	E		S		E		E	
S	I	E	S	T	A		E	N	T	E	R

71

	G		T		L			A		H	
H	I	G	H	N	O	O	N		N	O	A	H
	L		A		N		O	N	S	
S	T	A	L	A	G		T	A	U	N	T
		I		S		H		A		I	
	G	I	A	N	T	K	I	L	L	I	N	G
	H		A		N			G		
L	O	O	K	I	N	G	G	L	A	S	S
	S		I		D		D		L		
	T	U	T	T	I		O	B	L	O	N	G
	I		B		N		I		D		A
A	N	N	A		G	U	N	G	A	D	I	N
	G		G			G		Y		L	

72

R	E	P	L	Y	P	A	I	D		O	
U		R		E		M		I	M	P	I
D	E	M	E	R	A	R	A		S		T
	I		R		R	E	M	A	I	N	
I	N	C	A		K		Y	E	C	
G		P	R	O	B	L	E	M	I	S	T
	H		R		L		B		
S	Q	U	A	R	E	M	I	L	E		S
U		E	A	S		R	O	P	E	
J	O	P	L	I	N		M	E		E
R		I		W	A	N	D	E	R	I	E	D
O	U	S	T		A		Y		N	D
M		E	A	R	N	E	S	T	L	Y

185

73

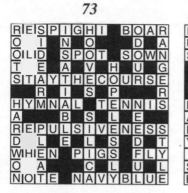

74

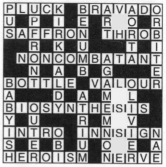

75

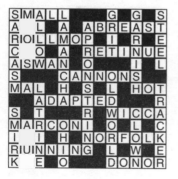

76

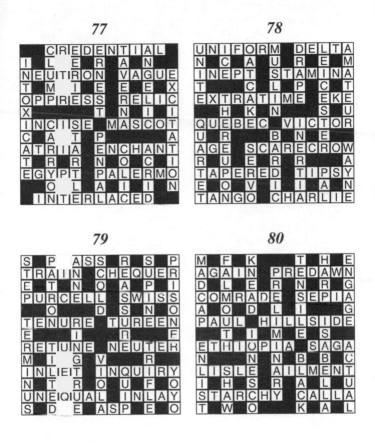

77 **78**

79 **80**

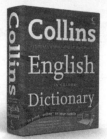